Higher
Mathematics
Practice Papers for SQA Exams

Robert Barclay

Contents

HODDER
GIBSON
AN HACHETTE UK COMPANY

The Publishers would like to thank the following for permission to reproduce copyright material:

Acknowledgements: Formulae list (p.vii) and exam rubrics at the start of each paper copyright © Scottish Qualifications Authority.

Every effort has been made to trace all copyright holders, but if any have been inadvertently overlooked the Publishers will be pleased to make the necessary arrangements at the first opportunity.

Although every effort has been made to ensure that website addresses are correct at time of going to press, Hodder Gibson cannot be held responsible for the content of any website mentioned in this book. It is sometimes possible to find a relocated web page by typing in the address of the home page for a website in the URL window of your browser.

Hachette UK's policy is to use papers that are natural, renewable and recyclable products and made from wood grown in sustainable forests. The logging and manufacturing processes are expected to conform to the environmental regulations of the country of origin.

Orders: please contact Bookpoint Ltd, 130 Park Drive, Milton Park, Abingdon, Oxon OX14 4SE. Telephone: (44) 01235 827720. Fax: (44) 01235 400454. Lines are open 9.00–5.00, Monday to Saturday, with a 24-hour message answering service. Visit our website at www.hoddereducation.co.uk. Hodder Gibson can be contacted direct on: Tel: 0141 333 4650; Fax: 0141 404 8188; email: hoddergibson@hodder.co.uk

Cover photo © jlpfeifer/123RF.com
Illustrations by Aptara, Inc.
Typeset in Din-Regular 12/14 pts by Aptara Inc.
Printed in the UK

A catalogue record for this title is available from the British Library.

ISBN: 978 1 5104 1499 0

Introduction

Higher Mathematics

The course

The Higher Mathematics course is designed to enable learners to build upon and extend the knowledge, understanding and skills which they have acquired while completing the National 5 Mathematics course. Before starting this course you should therefore already be proficient in the skills required to pass National 5 Mathematics or equivalent.

The course comprises three component Units - Expressions & Functions, Relationships & Calculus and Applications – and the course assessment, i.e. the examination.

As you work through the course you will develop your knowledge, understanding and skills in algebra, geometry, trigonometry, calculus and reasoning.

Throughout the course you will be expected to use reasoning skills to:

- interpret a situation where mathematics can be used and identify a strategy
- explain a solution and/or relate it to context.

The course content is summarised below.

Expressions & Functions	Relationships & Calculus	Applications

■ Logarithms and exponents
■ Trigonometric expressions
  ■ addition formulae
  ■ double angle formulae
  ■ wave function
■ Completing the square in a quadratic expression
■ Graphs of functions
■ Composite and inverse functions
■ Vectors
	■ Polynomials
	■ Quadratics
	■ Trigonometric equations
	■ Differentiating functions
	■ Using differentiation
	  ■ equation of tangent to curve
	  ■ increasing and decreasing functions
	  ■ curve sketching
	■ Integrating functions
	■ Using integration
	  ■ definite integrals
		■ Straight line
		■ Circle
		■ Recurrence relations
		■ Using differentiation
		  ■ optimisation problems
		  ■ rate of change problems
		■ Using integration
		  ■ area
		  ■ rate of change problems

Assessment

To gain the course award, you must pass the three units and the examination.

The units are assessed internally on a pass/fail basis.

The examination is set and marked by the SQA.

It tests skills beyond the minimum competence required for the units.

The number of marks and the times allotted for the examination papers are as follows:

- Paper 1 (non-calculator)   60 marks   1 hour 10 minutes
- Paper 2   70 marks   1 hour 30 minutes

The course award is graded A–D, the grade being determined by the total mark you score in the examination.

The examination tests skills beyond the minimum competence required for the units. Both papers contain short and extended response questions.

The examination is designed so that approximately 65% of the marks will be available for level C responses.

Some questions will assess only operational skills (65% of the marks) but other questions will require both operational and reasoning skills (35% of the marks).

Further details can be found in the Higher Mathematics section on the SQA website: http://www.sqa.org.uk/sqa/47910.html.

Some tips for achieving a good mark

Build your confidence

It is important that you go into the examination with confidence. Confidence comes through success. If you can answer questions correctly it breeds confidence and belief, but if you fail to answer questions correctly it can lead to self-doubt. The key to success is preparation. In order to build your confidence, work hard throughout the year to consolidate your strengths while trying to work on areas where there is room for improvement. Don't be too hard on yourself. Remember that you could pass the examination with a score of 50% so you are allowed to make mistakes. You do not need to be a brilliant mathematician to pass Higher Mathematics. The students who work hardest are those who usually perform best in the examination. So the key to success is to practise, practise, practise!

Practise! Practise! Practise!

DOING maths questions is the most effective use of your study time. You will benefit much more from spending 30 minutes doing maths questions than spending several hours copying out notes or reading a maths textbook.

Practise doing the type of questions that are likely to appear in the exam. Work through these practice papers and past SQA Higher Mathematics papers. Use the marking instructions to check your answers and to understand what the examiners are looking for. Ask your teacher for help if you get stuck.

Basic skills

You must practise essential basic skills for Higher Mathematics throughout the duration of this course; for example, numerical calculations, manipulating algebraic expressions, expanding brackets, solving equations and working with exact values in trigonometric expressions and equations.

Topics introduced at National 5

You must ensure that you are proficient in the basic skills in topics which are introduced at National 5 (for example, vectors, indices, completing the square and problems involving straight lines) before developing more advanced skills in them during the Higher course.

Non-routine problems

It is important to practise non-routine problems, particularly in unfamiliar contexts, as often as possible throughout the course, particularly if you are aiming for an A or B pass in Higher Mathematics.

Graph sketching

Graph sketching is an important and integral part of Mathematics. Ensure that you practise sketching graphs on plain paper whenever possible throughout this course. Neither squared nor graph paper are allowed in the Higher Mathematics examination.

Show all working clearly

The instructions on the front of the exam paper state that 'Full credit will be given only to solutions which contain appropriate working'. A 'correct' answer with no working may only be awarded partial marks or even no marks at all. An incomplete answer will be awarded marks for any appropriate working. Attempt every question, even if you are not sure whether you are correct or not. Your solution may contain working which will gain some marks. A blank response is certain to be awarded no marks. Never score out working unless you have something better to replace it with.

Make drawings

Try drawing what you visualise as the 'picture', described within the wording of each relevant question. This is a mathematical skill expected of most candidates at Higher level. Making a rough sketch of the diagram in your answer booklet may also help you interpret the question and achieve more marks.

Extended response questions

You should look for connections between parts of questions, particularly where there are three or four sections to a question. These are almost always linked and, in some instances, an earlier result in part a) or b) is needed, and using it will avoid further repeated work.

Notation

In all questions make sure that you use the correct notation. In particular, for integration questions, remember to include '*dx*' within your integral.

Radians

Remember to work in radians when attempting any question involving both trigonometry and calculus.

Simplify

Get into the habit of simplifying expressions before doing any further work with them. This should make all subsequent work easier. Be aware that numerical values in final answers must be simplified as far as possible.

Good luck!

Remember that the rewards for passing Higher Mathematics are well worth it! Your pass will help you get the future you want for yourself. In the examination, be confident in your own ability; if you're not sure how to answer a question trust your instincts and just give it a go anyway – keep calm and don't panic! GOOD LUCK!

Revision grid

Topic	A Paper 1	A Paper 2	B Paper 1	B Paper 2	C Paper 1	C Paper 2
Functions and Graphs	2, 6, 9, 11		2, 10	2	7, 9a), 11	1, 5, 8
Quadratics	4	2		1, 10	6, 9b), 14b)	
Polynomials		5a)	12			9
Recurrence Relations	10			7	2	
Logarithms and Exponentials	8, 12	7	6	9, 11	10, 13	
The Straight Line		1		5a)b)	4	2
The Circle	1	4	7	3, 5c)	14a)	3
Vectors	5, 14	6	3, 9	4	3	12
Trigonometric Formulae	15	10a)	8	13		7, 13
The Wave Function		8	13			11
Differentiation	3		4	6		4
Applications of Differentiation	7, 16	3	1	12a)b)	1, 8	10
Integration	13	10b)	5		5, 12	
Applications of Integration		5b), 9	11	8, 12c)		6

Formulae list

Circle:

The equation $x^2 + y^2 + 2gx + 2fy + c = 0$ represents a circle centre $(-g, -f)$ and radius $\sqrt{g^2 + f^2 - c}$.

The equation $(x - a)^2 + (y - b)^2 = r^2$ represents a circle centre (a, b) and radius r.

Scalar Product:

$\mathbf{a}.\mathbf{b} = |\mathbf{a}||\mathbf{b}| \cos \theta$, where θ is the angle between $\mathbf{a}$ and $\mathbf{b}$

or

$\mathbf{a}.\mathbf{b} = a_1 b_1 + a_2 b_2 + a_3 b_3$ where $\mathbf{a} = \begin{pmatrix} a_1 \\ a_2 \\ a_3 \end{pmatrix}$ and $\mathbf{b} = \begin{pmatrix} b_1 \\ b_2 \\ b_3 \end{pmatrix}$.

Trigonometric formulae:

$\sin(A \pm B) = \sin A \cos B \pm \cos A \sin B$

$\cos(A \pm B) = \cos A \cos B \mp \sin A \sin B$

$$\sin 2A = 2 \sin A \cos A$$

$$\cos 2A = \cos^2 A - \sin^2 A$$

$$= 2 \cos^2 A - 1$$

$$= 1 - 2 \sin^2 A$$

Table of standard derivatives:

$f(x)$	$f'(x)$
$\sin ax$	$a \cos ax$
$\cos ax$	$-a \sin ax$

Table of standard integrals:

$f(x)$	$\int f(x)\,dx$
$\sin ax$	$-\dfrac{1}{a} \cos ax + c$
$\cos ax$	$\dfrac{1}{a} \sin ax + c$

Higher
Mathematics

Paper 1 (non-calculator)

Total marks: 60

Attempt ALL questions.

You may NOT use a calculator.

Full credit will be given only to solutions which contain appropriate working.

State the units for your answer where appropriate.

Answers obtained by readings from scale drawings will not receive any credit.

Write your answers clearly and make sure you **identify the question number you are attempting**. In the actual exam, you will be given an answer booklet in which to write your answers.

Use **blue** or **black** ink.

In the actual exam, you must give your answer booklet to the Invigilator before leaving the examination room; if you do not, you may lose all the marks for the paper.

MARKS

1 P(–1, 4) and Q(5, –6) are points on the circumference of a circle.

   PQ is a diameter.

   Find the equation of the circle.   3

2 Functions $f(x) = \dfrac{1}{x+2}$ and $g(x) = 3x - 4$ are defined on suitable domains.

   a) Find an expression for $h(x)$ where $h(x) = f(g(x))$.   2

   b) What value of x cannot be in the domain of h?   1

3 Given that $f(x) = \dfrac{2x^3 - 1}{x^2}$, find $f'(x)$.   3

4 Find the range of values of k for which $kx^2 - 4x + 3 = 0$ has no real roots.   3

5 The vector $a\mathbf{i} - b\mathbf{j} + \mathbf{k}$ is perpendicular to both the vectors $2\mathbf{i} - \mathbf{j} + 4\mathbf{k}$ and $-3\mathbf{i} + \mathbf{j} - \mathbf{k}$.

   Find the values of a and b.   3

MARKS

6 The diagram shows a sketch of the function $y = f(x)$.

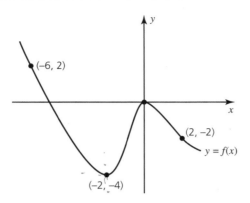

(−6, 2)

(2, −2)

$y = f(x)$

(−2, −4)

a) Sketch the graph of $y = f(2x)$.

1

b) Sketch the graph of $y = 2 - f(2x)$.

2

7 Find algebraically the values of x for which the function $f(x) = x^3 + x^2 - 8x + 3$ is strictly increasing.

4

8 Evaluate $\log_4 12 - \left(\log_4 8 + \dfrac{1}{2}\log_4 36 \right)$.

4

9 The diagram shows the graph of $y = 3\sin\left(x + \dfrac{\pi}{6}\right) + 1$, for $0 \le x \le 2\pi$.

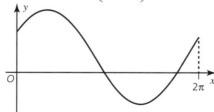

2π

Find the co-ordinates of the maximum turning point.

3

10 With suitable values for u_0 and v_0, two sequences are generated by the recurrence relations $u_{n+1} = pu_n + 3$ and $v_{n+1} = p^2 v_n + 5$.

The two sequences approach the same limit as $n \to \infty$.

Determine the value of p and evaluate the limit.

5

11 The diagram below shows the graph with equation $y = f(x)$, where $f(x) = kx^2(x-a)$.

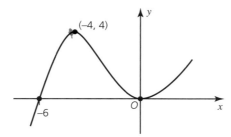

Find the values of a and k.

2

12 Solve the equation $\log_2(x+1) + \log_2(5-3x) = 2$, where $-1 < x < \dfrac{5}{3}$.

4

13 Find $\displaystyle\int \sqrt{2x-3}\,dx$.

3

14 The diagram shows a right-angled triangle whose sides represent the vectors **a**, **b** and **c**.

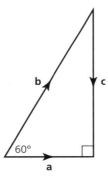

The angle between vectors **a** and **b** is 60°.

If $|\mathbf{a}| = 1$ and $|\mathbf{b}| = 2$, evaluate $\mathbf{b}.(\mathbf{a}+\mathbf{c})$.

3

15 a) If $\tan x = \dfrac{1}{4}, 0 \le x \le \dfrac{\pi}{2}$, find the exact value of $\sin 2x$.

3

b) Hence find the exact value of $\sin 4x$.

3

16 A piece of land beside a stone wall is to be fenced off with 270 metres of fencing to make two identical rectangular enclosures with sides of length x metres and y metres as shown in the diagram.

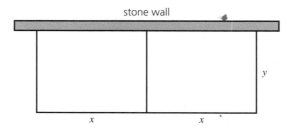

Only three sides of each enclosure need fencing since the wall provides the fourth boundary.

a) Show that the combined area of the enclosures is given by $A = 180x - \dfrac{4}{3}x^2$.

3

b) Find the maximum area that can be fenced off.

5

END OF PAPER 1

Paper 2

MARKS

1 A triangle PQR has vertices P(–7, 3), Q(9, 5) and R(4, –5).

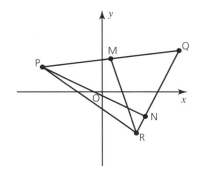

a)	Find the equation of the median RM.	3
b)	Find the equation of the altitude PN.	3
c)	Find the co-ordinates of the point of intersection of RM and PN.	3

2 Express $2x^2 - 12x + 11$ in the form $a(x + b)^2 + c$.   3

3 Find the equation of the tangent to the curve $y = (x - 3)^4$ at the point (2, 1).   3

4 The circle with centre C_1 has equation $x^2 + y^2 - 16x - 2y + 60 = 0$.

The line RP is a tangent to this circle at the point P(7, 3).

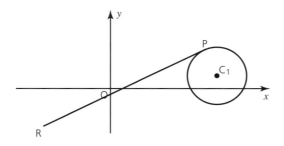

a) Show that the equation of this tangent is $x - 2y = 1$.

4

The circle with centre C_2 has equation $x^2 + y^2 + 10x - 4y + 9 = 0$.

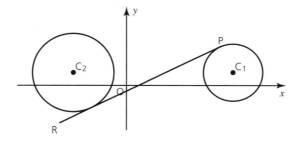

b) Show that RP is also a tangent to this circle.

4

5 The curve shown in the diagram below has equation $y = x^3 - x^2 - 6x + 2$.

The line PQ, with equation $5x + y - 1 = 0$, is a tangent to the curve at the point Q(1, −4) and intersects the curve at the point P.

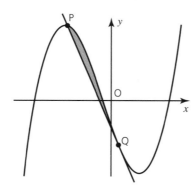

a) Find the co-ordinates of P.

5

b) Find the shaded area enclosed between the line and the curve.

5

6   ABCD, EFGH is a cuboid.

M is the midpoint of HG.

N lies one third of the way along FG.

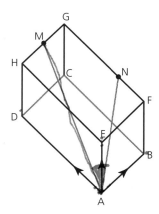

$\overrightarrow{AB}$, $\overrightarrow{AD}$ and $\overrightarrow{AE}$ are represented by the vectors $\begin{pmatrix} 2 \\ 4 \\ 0 \end{pmatrix}$, $\begin{pmatrix} -6 \\ 3 \\ 3 \end{pmatrix}$ and $\begin{pmatrix} 2 \\ -1 \\ 5 \end{pmatrix}$ respectively.

a) Calculate the components of $\overrightarrow{AM}$.   2

b) Calculate the components of $\overrightarrow{AN}$.   2

c) Calculate the size of angle MAN.   5

7   The mass, m_t grams, of the radioactive substance radium-226 remaining after t years is given by the formula $m_t = m_0 e^{-0.0004332t}$, where m_0 is the initial mass of the substance.

a) If the original mass is 140 grams, find the mass after 100 years.   2

b) The half-life of any substance is the time taken for the mass to decrease to half of the initial mass.

Find the half-life of radium-226.   4

8   **a)** Express $15\sin x + 8\cos x$ in the form $k\sin(x+a)$ where $k>0$ and $0 \le a \le 360$.   4

b) Hence solve the equation $15\sin x + 8\cos x = 10$ for $0 \le x \le 360$.   4

MARKS

9 The rate of change of the height, h metres, of a ball which is thrown vertically upwards is given by $\dfrac{dh}{dt} = 20 - kt$.

- t is the elapsed time, in seconds, since the ball is thrown.
- k is a constant.
- Initially, the height of the ball is 2 metres.
- The ball reaches a height of 15 metres after 1 second.

Express h in terms of t.

6

10 In the diagram, angle ABC $= 2x$ and angle CBD $= x$.

a) Show that $\cos \text{ABD} = 4\cos^3 x - 3\cos x$.

5

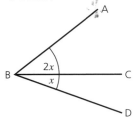

b) Hence find $\int \cos^3 x\, dx$.

3

END OF PAPER 2

Higher
Mathematics

HODDER
GIBSON
LEARN MORE

Paper 1 (non-calculator)

Total marks: 60

Attempt ALL questions.

You may NOT use a calculator.

Full credit will be given only to solutions which contain appropriate working.

State the units for your answer where appropriate.

Answers obtained by readings from scale drawings will not receive any credit.

Write your answers clearly and make sure you **identify the question number you are attempting**. In the actual exam, you will be given an answer booklet in which to write your answers.

Use **blue** or **black** ink.

In the actual exam, you must give your answer booklet to the Invigilator before leaving the examination room; if you do not, you may lose all the marks for the paper.

MARKS

1 Find the point on the curve with equation $y = 3x - x^2$ where the gradient of the tangent is 4.

4

2 The function $g(x) = 2 - 3x$ is defined on the set of real numbers.

   Find an expression for $g^{-1}(x)$.

3

3 P is the point (−2, 4, 1) and Q is (1, 4, −3).

   Find the components of a unit vector which is parallel to $\overrightarrow{PQ}$.

3

4 Given that $f(x) = 4(5 - 2x)^3$, find $f'(3)$.

3

5 Find the value of $\int_1^2 \dfrac{t^2 - 3}{3t^2}\,dt$.

5

6 Solve the equation $\log_5(x - 1) - 3\log_5 2 = 3$.

4

7 Find the equation of the tangent to the circle $x^2 + y^2 - 6x - 4y + 8 = 0$ at the point (5, 1).

4

8 If $x°$ is an acute angle such that $\cos x° = \dfrac{1}{7}$, show that $\cos(x + 60) = -\dfrac{11}{14}$.

5

9 The points A(1, −7, −15), B(7, 2, −3) and C(x, 8, 5) are collinear.

   Find the value of x.

2

10 The function $f(x) = 3^x - 3$ is defined on the set of real numbers.

The graph with equation $y = f(x)$ passes through the point R(2, 6) and cuts the y- and x-axes at P and Q respectively as shown in the diagram.

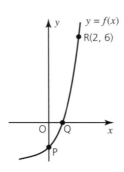

a) Find the co-ordinates of P and Q. 2

b) Sketch the graph with equation $y = \dfrac{1}{2} f(-x)$. 2

c) Find the co-ordinates of the image of R on the graph with equation $y = f(x+2) + 10$. 2

11 The diagram shows a sketch of part of the graph of $y = 4\sin 2x$.

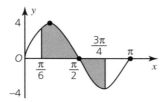

Find the total shaded area. 6

12 For the polynomial $2x^3 + 7x^2 + ax + b$,

- $x - 1$ is a factor
- 20 is the remainder when it is divided by $x + 3$.

a) Determine the values of a and b. 4

b) Hence factorise the polynomial completely. 3

13 a) Express $\cos x + \sin x$ in the form $k\cos(x - a)$ where $k > 0$ and $0 \le a \le 2\pi$. 4

b) Hence, or otherwise, sketch the curve with equation $y = \cos x + \sin x$ in the interval $0 \le x \le 2\pi$. 4

END OF PAPER 1

Paper 2

Total marks: 70

Attempt ALL questions.

You may use a calculator.

Full credit will be given only to solutions which contain appropriate working.

State the units for your answer where appropriate.

Answers obtained by readings from scale drawings will not receive any credit.

Write your answers clearly and make sure you **identify the question number you are attempting**. In the actual exam, you will be given an answer booklet in which to write your answers.

Use **blue** or **black** ink.

In the actual exam, you must give your answer booklet to the Invigilator before leaving the examination room; if you do not, you may lose all the marks for the paper.

MARKS

1 Solve $10 - 3x - x^2 < 0$, where x is a real number.   2

2 Functions $f(x) = \dfrac{1}{x+3}$ and $g(x) = \dfrac{1}{x} - 3$ are defined on suitable domains.

    a) Find an expression for $f(g(x))$.
        Give your answer in its simplest form.   3

    b) What is the connection between the functions f and g?   1

3 Two circles, with centres A and B, have equations $x^2 + y^2 - 4x - 60 = 0$ and $x^2 + y^2 - 20x - 30y + 300 = 0$ respectively.

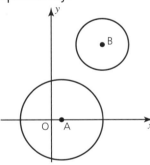

    a) Find the distance between the centres of the two circles.   3

    b) Hence, calculate the size of the smallest gap between the two circles as shown in the diagram.   3

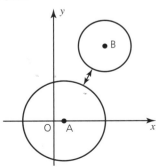

MARKS

4 OABCD is a pyramid.

A is the point (24, 0, 0), B is (24, 16, 0) and D is (12, 8, 20).

E divides DB in the ratio 3 : 1.

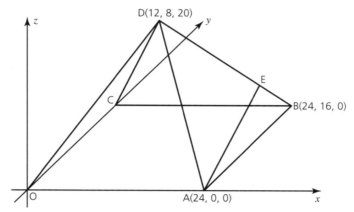

a) Find the co-ordinates of the point E. 2

b) Calculate the components of $\overrightarrow{AD}$ and $\overrightarrow{AE}$. 2

c) Calculate the size of angle DAE. 5

5 a) A chord joins the points P(−2, 0) and Q(3, 5) on a circle as shown in the diagram.

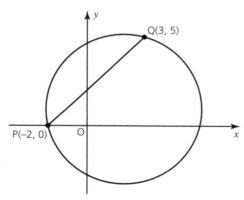

Show that the equation of the perpendicular bisector of chord PQ is $x + y = 3$. 4

b) The point C is the centre of the circle and RQ is the diameter with equation $y = 4x − 7$.

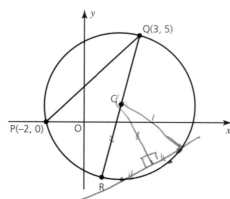

Find the co-ordinates of the point C. 3

c) Find the equation of the circle. 2

6 Given that $y = 2\cos 3x - \dfrac{1}{x^3}$, find $\dfrac{dy}{dx}$.

4

7 Rory puts £2100 into a bank account on the first of each month.

He spends 96% of the amount in the account by the end of the month.

The account earns no interest.

a) **(i)** Write down a recurrence relation for the amount of money, A_n, in his account on the first day of the nth month.

2

(ii) How much will be in the account in the long term on the first of each month?

1

b) Rory wants to have £2400 in the account in the long term on the first of each month.

What percentage of the money in the account should he spend each month?

3

8 A curve with equation $y = f(x)$ passes through the point $(2, -1)$ and is such that $f'(x) = 3 - \dfrac{4}{x^2}$.

Express $f(x)$ in terms of x.

4

9 The population of a city in the year 2015 was 243 500.

The population of the city t years after 2015 can be approximated by the formula $P = 243500e^{0.008t}$.

a) Find the population of the city in the year 2025.

2

b) How many years would it take for the population of the city to reach 330 000?

4

10 The roots of the equation $(x + 1)(x - k) = -1$ are equal.

Find the values of k.

5

11 Two variables, x and y, are related by the equation $y = be^{ax}$.

If $\log_e y$ is plotted against x, the following graph is obtained.

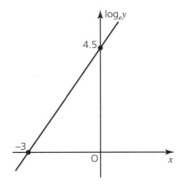

Find the values of a and b.

4

MARKS

12 Acceleration is defined as the rate of change of velocity. An object is travelling in a straight line. Its velocity, $v\,\text{m\,s}^{-1}$, t seconds after the start of its motion, is given by $v(t) = 1 + 5t - t^2$.

    a) Find a formula for $a(t)$, the acceleration of this object, t seconds after the start of its motion.

2

    b) How many seconds after the start of its motion does this object begin to decelerate?

2

    c) Velocity is defined as the rate of change of displacement. Find a formula for $s(t)$, the displacement of the object, given that $s(t) = 2$ when $t = 0$.

3

13 Solve $\cos 2\theta + \cos\theta = 0$ for $0 \le \theta < 2\pi$.

4

END OF PAPER 2

Higher Mathematics

Paper 1 (non-calculator)

C

Total marks: 60
Attempt ALL questions.
You may NOT use a calculator.
Full credit will be given only to solutions which contain appropriate working.
State the units for your answer where appropriate.
Answers obtained by readings from scale drawings will not receive any credit.
Write your answers clearly and make sure you **identify the question number you are attempting**. In the actual exam, you will be given an answer booklet in which to write your answers.
Use **blue** or **black** ink.
In the actual exam, you must give your answer booklet to the Invigilator before leaving the examination room; if you do not, you may lose all the marks for the paper.

MARKS

1 Find the equation of the tangent to the curve $y = x^4 - 3x^2 + x + 5$ at the point where $x = -1$.

4

2 A sequence is defined by the recurrence relation $u_{n+1} = au_n + b$, where $-1 < a < 1$ and $u_0 = 40$.

a) If $u_1 = 28$ and $u_2 = 19$, find the values of a and b.

4

b) Find the limit of this sequence as $n \to \infty$.

2

3 VPQRS is a pyramid with rectangular base PQRS.
T divides QR in the ratio $3:1$.

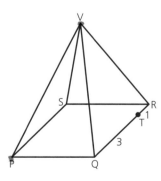

Relative to some appropriate axes,

$\overrightarrow{PQ}$ represents $5\mathbf{i} + 5\mathbf{j} - 5\mathbf{k}$

$\overrightarrow{PS}$ represents $4\mathbf{i} + 4\mathbf{j} + 8\mathbf{k}$

$\overrightarrow{PV}$ represents $6\mathbf{i} + 11\mathbf{j} + 9\mathbf{k}$

Find $\overrightarrow{VT}$ in component form.

3

4 PQRS is a parallelogram. P, Q and R have co-ordinates (–2, 1), (4, 10) and (6, –5).

Show that the equation of RS is $3x - 2y = 28$.

3

5 Find $\int x(x^2 + \sqrt{x})\,dx$.

4

6 a) Express $5 + 2x - x^2$ in the form $a - (x - b)^2$.

2

b) State the maximum value of $5 + 2x - x^2$ and give a reason for your answer.

2

7 The function $f(x) = \log_b(x + a)$ is defined on a suitable domain.

The graph with equation $y = f(x)$ is shown in the diagram below.

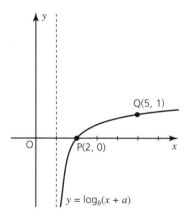

a) Find the values of a and b.

3

b) State the domain for $f(x)$.

1

c) Sketch the graph with equation $y = f^{-1}(x)$.

2

8 The volume of a sphere is given by the formula $V = \dfrac{4}{3}\pi r^3$.

Find the rate of change of V with respect to r, at $r = 5$.

2

9 a) $f(x) = 2x + 3$ and $g(x) = x^2 - k$ where k is a constant.
Find expressions for $f(g(x))$ and $g(f(x))$.

3

b) (i) Show that the equation $g(f(x)) - f(g(x))$ simplifies
to $2x^2 + 12x + 6 + k$.

1

(ii) Find the value of k for which the equation $2x^2 + 12x + 6 + k = 0$
has equal roots.

3

10 Two variables, x and y, are related by the equation $y = kx^n$.

If $\log_3 y$ is plotted against $\log_3 x$ the following graph is obtained.

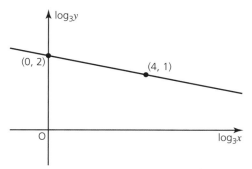

Find the values of k and n.

5

11 The diagram shows part of the graph of a function whose equation is of the form $y = p\cos(x + q) + r$

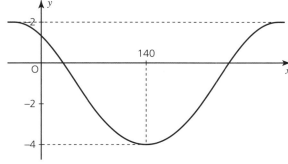

Write down the values of p, q and r.

3

12 Show that $\int_{\frac{\pi}{6}}^{\frac{5\pi}{12}} \cos\left(3\theta - \frac{\pi}{4}\right) d\theta = -\frac{\sqrt{2}}{6}$.

5

13 Show that the solution to the equation $e^{x+1} = e^x + 1$ is $x = \log_e\left(\frac{1}{e-1}\right)$.

3

14 A circle has centre $(0, t)$, $t > 0$, and radius 3 units.

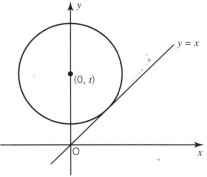

a) Write down the equation of the circle.

1

b) Given that the line $y = x$ is a tangent to the circle, find the exact value of t in its simplest form.

4

END OF PAPER 1

C

Paper 2

MARKS

1 Functions $f(x) = \sqrt{7 - 4x}$ and $g(x) = \dfrac{x^3 + 1}{2}$ are defined on suitable domains.

    a) Write down the range of values of x which cannot be in the domain of f.   1

    b) Find $g^{-1}(x)$.   3

2 ABCD is a kite as shown in the diagram with B the point (4, 8) and D the point (12, −4).

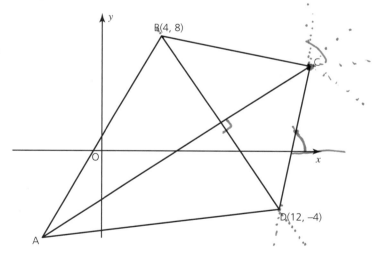

    a) Find the equation of the line AC, a diagonal of the kite.   4

    b) The line DC has equation $5x - y = 64$.

        (i) Find the co-ordinates of the point C.   2

        (ii) Calculate the angle that DC makes with the positive direction of the x-axis.   2

3 The diagram shows two circles which touch at the point P(1, 3).

The radius of the larger circle is double the radius of the smaller circle.

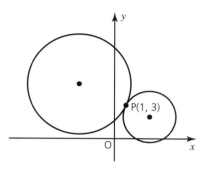

One of the circles has equation $x^2 + y^2 + 6x - 10y + 14 = 0$.

Find the equation of the other circle.

5

4 Given that $y = \sqrt{1+x^2} + \sin^2 x$, find $\dfrac{dy}{dx}$.

5

5 The diagram shows the graph of a function f.

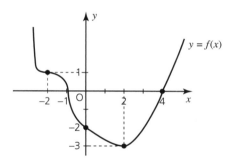

f has a point of inflexion at $(-2, 1)$ and a minimum turning point at $(2, -3)$.

Sketch the graph of the derived function f'.

3

MARKS

6 Calculate the shaded area enclosed by the parabolas with equations
$y = 2 + 9x - 3x^2$ and $y = 2 + x - x^2$.

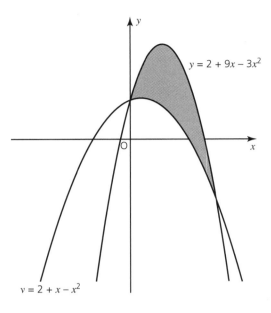

6

7 Solve $3 \sin 2x = 2 \cos x$ for $0 \leq x < 360$.

4

8 The diagram below shows the graph with equation $y = f(x)$, where
$f(x) = k(x + a)(x + b)^2$.

Find the values of a, b and k.

3

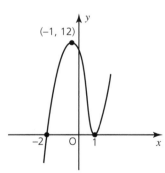

9 a) Show that $(x - 2)$ is a factor of $f(x) = x^3 - 9x^2 + 24x - 20$.

2

b) Hence solve the equation $x^3 - 9x^2 + 24x - 20 = 0$.

3

10 A function f is defined on the domain $0 \leq x \leq 4$ by $f(x) = x^3 + x^2 - 5x - 2$.

Determine the maximum and minimum values of f.

7

11 a) Express $\sqrt{3}\cos x° + \sin x°$ in the form $k\cos(x - a)°$ where $k > 0$ and $0 \le a \le 360$.

4

b) The depth, d centimetres, of water in a harbour t hours after midnight is given by the formula $d = 220 + 70(\sqrt{3}\cos 30t° + \sin 30t°)$.

Express d in the form $220 + m\cos(30t - a)°$.

1

c) Hence find the depth of the water in the harbour at 'low-water' and determine the time that 'low-water' first occurs after midnight.

2

12 ABCD is a quadrilateral with vertices A(–1, 0, –3), B(2, 6, –6), C(8, 9, 6) and D(8, 3, 18).

a) The point E divides the line AC in the ratio $5:4$.
Find the co-ordinates of E.

2

b) Show that B, E and D are collinear.

3

c) Calculate the size of the acute angle between the diagonals of quadrilateral ABCD.

5

13 Show that $\dfrac{\sin 2x}{1 + \cos 2x} = \tan x$, where $0 < x < \dfrac{\pi}{2}$.

3

END OF PAPER 2

Higher Mathematics

Practice Paper A

Paper 1 (non-calculator)

Q.	Working	Mark		Note	Hint	HTP
1	$C = \left(\dfrac{-1+5}{2}, \dfrac{4+(-6)}{2}\right) = (2,-1)$	✓		Find centre.	C is the midpoint of PQ. CP (or CQ) is a radius.	Ch 8
	$r^2 = CP^2 = (2-(-1))^2 + (-1-4)^2$			Find the square of the radius.		
	$= 3^2 + (-5)^2$					
	$= 34$	✓				
	$(x-2)^2 + (y+1)^2 = 34$	✓	3	State equation of circle.		
2 a)	$f(3x-4) = \dfrac{1}{(3x-4)+2}$	✓		Start composite process.	$f(g(x)) = \dfrac{1}{g(x)+2}$	Ch 3
	$= \dfrac{1}{3x-2}$	✓	2	Find $h(x)$ in simplest form.		
b)	$x \neq \dfrac{2}{3}$	✓	1	State value.	$h(x)$ is undefined when $3x-2=0$.	
3	$f(x) = 2x - x^{-2}$	✓		Prepare to differentiate.	Rearrange $f(x)$ into the form $ax^n + bx^m$ before differentiating, i.e.	Ch 13
	$f'(x) = 2\ldots\ldots\ldots$	✓		Differentiate first term.	$\dfrac{2x^3-1}{x^2} = \dfrac{2x^3}{x^2} - \dfrac{1}{x^2}$	
	$= 2 + 2x^{-3}$	✓	3	Differentiate second term.	$= 2x - x^{-2}$	
4	$b^2 - 4ac < 0$	✓		Use discriminant < 0.	No real roots so $b^2 - 4ac < 0$.	Ch 4
	$a = k, b = -4, c = 3$	✓		Identify a, b and c.		
	$16 - 12k < 0$			Find range of values of k in simplest form.		
	$k > \dfrac{4}{3}$	✓	3			
5	$2a + b + 4 = 0$			Use perpendicular property to obtain pair of equations.	$\mathbf{u}, \mathbf{v}$ perpendicular $\Leftrightarrow \mathbf{u}.\mathbf{v} = 0$	Ch 9
	$-3a - b - 1 = 0$	✓				
	$\Rightarrow -a + 3 = 0$			Find value of a.		
	$a = 3$	✓				
	$b = -10$	✓	3	Find value of b.		

Q.	Working	Mark		Note	Hint	HTP
6 a)		✓	1	Compress horizontally by a factor of 2 with all points correctly annotated.	$f(x) \to f(2x)$ $\Rightarrow (x,y) \to (\frac{x}{2}, y)$ e.g. $(-6,2) \to (-3,2)$	Ch 3
b)		✓ ✓	 2	Reflect $y=f(2x)$ in x-axis. Then vertical translation of 2 units up with all points correctly annotated.	$2 - f(2x) = -f(2x) + 2$ $f(2x) \to -f(2x)$ $\qquad \to -f(2x) + 2$ $\Rightarrow (\frac{x}{2}, y) \to (\frac{x}{2}, -y)$ $\qquad \to (\frac{x}{2}, -y+2)$ e.g. $(-3,2) \to (-3,-2)$ $\qquad \to (-3,0)$	Ch 3
7	$f'(x) = 3x^2 + 2x - 8$ $3x^2 + 2x - 8 > 0$ $(3x-4)(x+2) > 0$ $x < -2, x > \frac{4}{3}$	✓ ✓ ✓ ✓	 4	Differentiate. Set derivative greater than 0. Factorise. Find correct range of values.	$f(x)$ is increasing when $f'(x) > 0$. Use a sketch graph of $y = (3x-4)(x+2)$ to solve $(3x-4)(x+2) > 0$. 	Ch 13
8	$\log_4 12 - (\log_4 8 + \log_4 36^{\frac{1}{2}})$ $= \log_4 12 - (\log_4 8 + \log_4 6)$ $= \log_4 12 - \log_4(8 \times 6)$ $= \log_4 12 - \log_4 48$ $= \log_4 \frac{12}{48}$ $= \log_4 \frac{1}{4}$ $= -1$	 ✓ ✓ ✓ ✓	 4	Use $n\log_a x$ $\quad = \log_a x^n$ Use $\log_a x + \log_a y$ $\quad = \log_a xy$ Use $\log_a x - \log_a y$ $\quad = \log_a \frac{x}{y}$ Evaluate.	Use the laws of logarithms to simplify the expression into the form $\log_4 a$. $\log_4 \frac{1}{4} = \log_4 4^{-1} = -1$	Ch 6

A

Q.	Working	Mark	Note	Hint	HTP
9	$y_{max} = 3 \times 1 + 1 = 4$ x_{max} occurs when $x + \dfrac{\pi}{6} = \dfrac{\pi}{2}$ $\Rightarrow x = \dfrac{\pi}{3}$ Maximum t.p. is $\left(\dfrac{\pi}{3}, 4\right)$	✓ ✓ ✓ 3	Find y_{max}. Start to find x_{max}. State co-ordinates of maximum turning point.	For any angle θ, the maximum value of $\sin \theta$ is 1 when $\theta = \dfrac{\pi}{2}$.	Ch 10
10	$\dfrac{3}{1-p} = \dfrac{5}{1-p^2}$ $3(1-p^2) = 5(1-p)$ $3 - 3p^2 = 5 - 5p$ $3p^2 - 5p + 2 = 0$ $(3p-2)(p-1) = 0$ $p = \dfrac{2}{3}, 1$ $p = \dfrac{2}{3}$ (since $-1 < p < 1$) $L = \dfrac{3}{1 - \dfrac{2}{3}}$ $= \dfrac{3}{\frac{1}{3}} = 9$	✓ ✓ ✓ ✓ ✓ 5	Equate the two limits. Rearrange equation into standard form. Solve equation. Reject invalid solution. Evaluate limit.	Substitute $a = p$ and $b = 3$ into the limit formula for u_{n+1} and $a = p^2$ and $b = 5$ into the limit formula for v_{n+1}. For $u_{n+1} = au_n + b$ a limit only exists when $-1 < a < 1$. $3 \div \dfrac{1}{3} = 3 \times \dfrac{3}{1} = 9$	Ch 5
11	one root $= -6$ $\Rightarrow$ one factor $= (x+6)$ $\Rightarrow a = -6$ $(-4, 4) \Rightarrow 4 = k \times (-4)^2 \times (-4+6)$ $4 = 32k$ $k = \dfrac{1}{8}$	 ✓ ✓ 2	Find a. Find k.	Graph crosses x-axis at $(-6, 0) \Rightarrow -6$ is a root. Since $(-4, 4)$ is on the curve substitute $x = -4$ and $f(x) = 4$ into the equation to find the value of k.	Ch 2

Q.	Working	Mark		Note	Hint	HTP
12	$\log_2[(x+1)(5-3x)]=2$	✓		Use $\log_a x + \log_a y$ $= \log_a xy$.	Use a law of logarithms to express the equation in the form $\log_2 f(x) = 2$ then convert into exponential form and solve the resulting quadratic equation.	Ch 6
	$(x+1)(5-3x)=2^2$	✓		Convert to exponential form.		
	$-3x^2+2x+5=4$			Express equation in standard quadratic form.		
	$3x^2-2x-1=0$	✓				
	$(3x+1)(x-1)=0$			Solve for x.		
	$x=-\dfrac{1}{3},\ x=1$	✓	4			
13	$\displaystyle\int (2x-3)^{\frac{1}{2}}\,dx$	✓		Prepare to integrate.	Express the integral in the form $\int (ax+b)^n\,dx$ before integrating.	Ch 15
	$=\dfrac{(2x-3)^{\frac{3}{2}}}{\frac{3}{2}}$	✓		Start to integrate.	$\displaystyle\int (ax+b)^n\,dx$ $=\dfrac{(ax+b)^{n+1}}{a(n+1)}+c$	
	$=\dfrac{(2x-3)^{\frac{3}{2}}}{\frac{3}{2}\times 2}$			Complete integration.	Remember to add c, the constant of integration.	
	$=\dfrac{(2x-3)^{\frac{3}{2}}}{3}+c$	✓	3			
14	Method 1			Method 1	Expand the brackets and then use $\mathbf{b.a}=|\mathbf{b}||\mathbf{a}|\cos\theta$ and $\mathbf{b.c}=|\mathbf{b}||\mathbf{c}|\cos\theta$.	Ch 9 and Ch 10
	$\mathbf{b.(a+c)}=\mathbf{b.a}+\mathbf{b.c}$	✓		Expand brackets.		
	$\mathbf{b.a}=2\times 1\times \cos 60$			Start to evaluate $\mathbf{b.a}$. and $\mathbf{b.c}$.		
	$\mathbf{b.c}=2\times \sqrt{3}\times \cos 150$	✓				
	$\mathbf{b.(a+c)}=1-3=-2$	✓		Evaluate $\mathbf{b.(a+c)}$.		

Q.	Working	Mark		Note	Hint	HTP
	Method 2 	✓		Method 2 Interpret pathway for **a** + **c**.		
	b.(a + c) $= 2 \times 2 \times \cos 120°$	✓		Start to evaluate **b.(a + c)**.		
	$= -2$	✓	3	Evaluate **b.(a + c)**.		

Q.	Working	Mark	Note	Hint	HTP
15 a)	$2\sin x\cos x$ $= 2\times\dfrac{1}{\sqrt{17}}\times\dfrac{4}{\sqrt{17}}$ $= \dfrac{8}{17}$	✓ ✓ ✓ 3	Use double angle formula. Substitute exact values of $\sin x$ and $\cos x$. Find exact value of $\sin 2x$.	Use $\sin 2x = 2\sin x\cos x$. Use $\tan x = \dfrac{1}{4} = \dfrac{\text{opposite}}{\text{adjacent}}$ and Pythagoras' theorem to sketch an appropriate right-angled triangle and hence deduce the values of $\sin x$ and $\cos x$.	Ch 11
b)	$2\sin 2x\cos 2x$ $= 2\times\dfrac{8}{17}\times\dfrac{15}{17}$ $= \dfrac{240}{289}$	✓ ✓ ✓ 3	Use double angle formula. Substitute exact values of $\sin 2x$ and $\cos 2x$. Find exact value of $\sin 4x$.	Use $\sin(2(2x)) = 2\sin 2x\cos 2x$. Use $\sin 2x = \dfrac{8}{17} = \dfrac{\text{opposite}}{\text{hypotenuse}}$ and Pythagoras' theorem to sketch an appropriate right-angled triangle and hence deduce the value of $\cos 2x$.	
16 a)	$2x + 3y = 270$ $y = 90 - \dfrac{2}{3}x$ $A = 2xy$ $= 2x\left(90 - \dfrac{2x}{3}\right)$ $= 180x - \dfrac{4}{3}x^2$	✓ ✓ ✓ 3	Form equation for length of fencing. Change subject to y. Show steps leading to given formula for area.	Area = length × breadth = $2xy$, but in order to obtain an expression in terms of only x, set up an equation modelling the total length of fencing. Use this equation to express y in terms of x and substitute for y in $A = 2xy$.	Ch 13

Q.	Working	Mark		Note	Hint	HTP
b)	$\dfrac{dA}{dx} = 180 - \dfrac{8}{3}x$	✓		Differentiate.	At stationary points $\dfrac{dA}{dx} = 0$.	Ch 13
	$180 - \dfrac{8}{3}x = 0$ at S.P.	✓		Set derivative equal to zero.	Alternatively $\dfrac{d^2A}{dx^2}$ may be used to justify the nature of stationary point as follows:	
	$x = 67.5$	✓		Solve for x. Justify nature of stationary point.		
	<table><tr><td>x</td><td colspan="3">← 67.5 →</td></tr><tr><td>$\dfrac{dA}{dx}$</td><td>+</td><td>0</td><td>−</td></tr><tr><td>slope</td><td>/</td><td>—</td><td>\</td></tr></table>				$\dfrac{d^2A}{dx^2} = -\dfrac{8}{3}$, hence a maximum since $\dfrac{d^2A}{dx^2} < 0$.	
	Hence $x = 67.5$ gives a maximum value for the area.	✓				
	$y = 90 - \dfrac{2}{3} \times 67.5 = 45$			Find maximum area.		
	$A = 2 \times 67.5 \times 45 = 6075\text{m}^2$	✓	5			

Paper 2

A

Q.	Working	Mark		Note	Hint	HTP
1 a)	$M = (1, 4)$	✓		Calculate midpoint of PQ.	Median RM is a line from R to the midpoint of PQ.	Ch 7
	$m_{RM} = -3$	✓		Calculate gradient of median.		
	$y + 5 = -3(x - 4)$			Find equation of median.		
	$3x + y = 7$	✓	3		Simplify the equation. (Any equivalent simplified version is acceptable.)	
b)	$m_{QR} = 2$	✓		Calculate gradient of QR.	Altitude PN is perpendicular to QR, hence $m_{PN} \times m_{QR} = -1$.	
	$m_{PN} = -\dfrac{1}{2}$	✓		Calculate gradient of PN.		
	$y - 3 = -\dfrac{1}{2}(x - (-7))$			Find equation of altitude.	Simplify the equation. (Any equivalent simplified version is acceptable.)	
	$x + 2y = -1$	✓	3			
c)	e.g. $3x + y = 7$			Start to solve simultaneous equations.	Use simultaneous equations to find where the two lines intersect.	
	$\quad\quad x + 2y = -1$					
	so $6x + 2y = 14$					
	$\quad\quad x + 2y = -1$	✓				
	so $x = 3$ (or $y = -2$)	✓		Calculate x- or y-co-ordinate.		
	$(3, -2)$	✓	3	Find co-ordinates of point of intersection.		
2	$2(x^2 - 6x) + 11$	✓		Use common factor.	Complete square for $2(x^2 - 6x)$ first, then add the 11 at the end.	Ch 4
	$2[(x - 3)^2 - 9] + 11$	✓		Start to complete square.		
	$2(x - 3)^2 - 18 + 11$			Complete process.		
	$2(x - 3)^2 - 7$	✓	3			
3	$\dfrac{dx}{dy} = 4(x - 3)^3$	✓		Differentiate.	The gradient of the tangent is the value of $\dfrac{dx}{dy}$ when $x = 2$.	Ch 13
	At $x = 2$, $\dfrac{dx}{dy} = 4(2 - 3)^3$			Evaluate derivative.		
	$\quad\quad\quad = -4$	✓				
	$y - 1 = -4(x - 2)$			Find equation of tangent.	Simplify the equation. (Any equivalent simplified version is acceptable.)	
	$\Leftrightarrow y = -4x + 9$	✓	3			

Q.	Working	Mark		Note	Hint	HTP
4 a)	centre $C_1 = (8, 1)$	✓		Find co-ordinates of centre C_1.	Find the equation of the line through $P(7, 3)$ which is perpendicular to radius C_1P. Tangent RP is perpendicular to radius C_1P hence $m_{RP} \times m_{C_1P} = -1$.	Ch 8
	$m_{radius} = \dfrac{3-1}{7-8} = -2$	✓		Find gradient of radius C_1P.		
	$m_{tangent} = \dfrac{1}{2}$	✓		Find gradient of tangent RP.		
	$y - 3 = \dfrac{1}{2}(x - 7)$			Show steps leading to required equation.	Since the answer is given, show all the steps from $y - 3 = \dfrac{1}{2}(x - 7)$ to the required equation.	
	$\Leftrightarrow 2y - 6 = x - 7$					
	$\Leftrightarrow x - 2y = 1$	✓	4			
b)	$(2y + 1)^2 + y^2$ $+ 10(2y + 1) - 4y + 9 = 0$	✓		Substitute $x = 2y + 1$ into equation of circle.	Use simultaneous equations (substitution method) to find possible points of intersection of the line and circle.	
	$5y^2 + 20y + 20 = 0$	✓		Express in standard quadratic form.		
	$b^2 - 4ac = 20^2 - 4 \times 5 \times 20$			Show that $b^2 - 4ac = 0$.	Use $b^2 - 4ac$ to show that there is only one point of contact.	
	$\qquad = 400 - 400$					
	$\qquad = 0$	✓				
	therefore equal roots			State conclusion.	Remember to state conclusion with justification.	
	therefore tangent	✓	4			
5 a)	$x^3 - x^2 - 6x + 2 = -5x + 1$			Form equation and rearrange into standard form.	Set equation of curve equal to equation of line, rearrange into standard form and solve.	Ch 2
	$x^3 - x^2 - x + 1 = 0$	✓				
	$\begin{array}{c|cccc} 1 & 1 & -1 & -1 & 1 \\ & & & & \\ \hline & & & & \end{array}$			Set up synthetic division table.		
		✓				
	$\begin{array}{c|cccc} 1 & 1 & -1 & -1 & 1 \\ & & 1 & 0 & -1 \\ \hline & 1 & 0 & -1 & 0 \end{array}$			Complete table and find quadratic factor.		
	$(x - 1)(x^2 - 1) = 0$	✓				
	$(x - 1)^2(x + 1) = 0$			Find x-co-ordinate of P.		
	$x = \pm 1$					
	$x_P = -1$	✓				
	$y_P = -5 \times -1 + 1 = 6$			State co-ordinates of P.	Remember to state the co-ordinates of P.	
	$P(-1, 6)$	✓	5			

Q.	Working	Mark	Note	Hint	HTP
b)	$\displaystyle\int_{-1}^{1} \ldots\ldots$	✓	Know to integrate and interpret limits.	Use $\displaystyle\int_{a}^{b}$ upper-lower. The limits are the x-co-ordinates of P and Q.	Ch 14
	$\displaystyle\int_{-1}^{1}(x^3 - x^2 - 6x + 2 \\ \qquad -(-5x+1))\,dx$		Use $\int$ curve-line.		
	$= \displaystyle\int_{-1}^{1}(x^3 - x^2 - x + 1)\,dx$	✓		$\left(\dfrac{1}{4} - \dfrac{1}{3} - \dfrac{1}{2} + 1\right)$	
	$\left[\dfrac{x^4}{4} - \dfrac{x^3}{3} - \dfrac{x^2}{2} + x\right]_{-1}^{1}$	✓	Integrate.	$-\left(\dfrac{1}{4} + \dfrac{1}{3} - \dfrac{1}{2} - 1\right)$	
	$= \left(\dfrac{1}{4} - \dfrac{1}{3} - \dfrac{1}{2} + 1\right)$		Substitute limits.	$= \dfrac{1}{4} - \dfrac{1}{4} - \dfrac{1}{3} - \dfrac{1}{3}$	
	$\quad -\left(\dfrac{1}{4} + \dfrac{1}{3} - \dfrac{1}{2} - 1\right)$	✓		$-\dfrac{1}{2} + \dfrac{1}{2} + 1 + 1$	
	$= 1\dfrac{1}{3}$ units^2	✓ 5	Evaluate area.	$= -\dfrac{2}{3} + 2$ $= 1\dfrac{1}{3}$	
6 a)	$\overrightarrow{AM} = \overrightarrow{AD} + \overrightarrow{DH} + \overrightarrow{HM}$ $= \overrightarrow{AD} + \overrightarrow{AE} + \dfrac{1}{2}\overrightarrow{AB}$	✓	Express $\overrightarrow{AM}$ in terms of $\overrightarrow{AB}$, $\overrightarrow{AD}$ and $\overrightarrow{AE}$.	Vectors which have the same direction and magnitude are equal, e.g. $\overrightarrow{DH} = \overrightarrow{AE}$.	Ch 9
	$= \begin{pmatrix} -3 \\ 4 \\ 8 \end{pmatrix}$	✓ 2	Find components of $\overrightarrow{AM}$.		
b)	$\overrightarrow{AN} = \overrightarrow{AB} + \overrightarrow{BF} + \overrightarrow{FN}$ $= \overrightarrow{AB} + \overrightarrow{AE} + \dfrac{1}{3}\overrightarrow{AD}$	✓	Express $\overrightarrow{AN}$ in terms of $\overrightarrow{AB}$, $\overrightarrow{AD}$ and $\overrightarrow{AN}$.	Vectors which have the same direction and magnitude are equal, e.g. $\overrightarrow{BF} = \overrightarrow{AE}$.	
	$= \begin{pmatrix} 2 \\ 4 \\ 6 \end{pmatrix}$	✓ 2	Find components of $\overrightarrow{AN}$.		
c)	$\cos MAN = \dfrac{\overrightarrow{AM}.\overrightarrow{AN}}{|\overrightarrow{AM}||\overrightarrow{AN}|}$	✓	Use scalar product applied to correct angle.	Use vectors that both point away from the vertex of the angle.	
	$\overrightarrow{AM}.\overrightarrow{AN} = 58$	✓	Find scalar product.		
	$|\overrightarrow{AM}| = \sqrt{89}$	✓	Find $|\overrightarrow{AM}|$.		
	$|\overrightarrow{AN}| = \sqrt{56}$	✓	Find $|\overrightarrow{AN}|$.	Don't approximate values of surds, e.g. $\sqrt{89} = 9.4$ as premature rounding may lead to an incorrect final answer.	
	angle $MAN = 34.8^{\circ}$	✓ 5	Find angle.		

A

Q.	Working	Mark		Note	Hint	HTP
7 a)	$m_{100} = 140 \times e^{-0.0004332 \times 100}$	✓		Substitute for m_0 and t in formula.		Ch 6
	$= 134$ grams	✓	2	Evaluate formula.		
b)	$\frac{1}{2}m_0 = m_0 e^{-0.0004332t}$	✓		Interpret half-life.	The half-life is the time for which $m_t = \frac{1}{2}m_0$.	
	$e^{-0.0004332t} = \frac{1}{2}$	✓		Process equation.		
	$-0.0004332t = \ln\left(\frac{1}{2}\right)$	✓		Write in logarithmic form.	Remember $e^x = y \Leftrightarrow x = \ln y$	
	$t = \dfrac{\ln\left(\frac{1}{2}\right)}{-0.0004332}$			Solve to find half-life.	Don't approximate the value of $\ln\left(\frac{1}{2}\right)$ as premature	
	$= 1600$ years	✓	4		rounding may lead to an incorrect final answer.	
8 a)	$15\sin x + 8\cos x =$ $k(\sin x \cos a$ $+ \cos x \sin a)$	✓		Use addition formula.	Use the expansion for $\sin(A+B)$ from the formula list.	Ch 12
	$k\cos a = 15,\ k\sin a = 8$	✓		Equate coefficients.		
	$k = \sqrt{15^2 + 8^2} = 17$	✓		Find k.		
	$a = \tan^{-1}\left(\frac{8}{15}\right) = 28$			Find a and state expression in required form.		
	$15\sin x + 8\cos x =$ $17\sin(x+28)$	✓	4			
b)	$17\sin(x+28) = 10$	✓		Equate wave function with 10.	Use the answer to part a) to rewrite the equation in a form that is easier to solve.	
	$\sin(x+28) = \frac{10}{17}$	✓		Rearrange equation.		
	$x + 28 = 36, 144$	✓		Solve for $x+28$.	$\sin(x+28)$ is positive. There are solutions in the 1st and 2nd quadrants.	
	$x = 8, 116$	✓	4	Solve for x.		

Q.	Working	Mark		Note	Hint	HTP
9	$h = \int (20 - kt)\,dt$	✓		Know to integrate.	Integrate $\dfrac{dh}{dt}$ to obtain h, since integration is the inverse of differentiation.	Ch 14
	$= 20t\ldots\ldots$	✓		Integrate first term.		
	$= 20t - \dfrac{kt^2}{2} + \ldots.$			Complete integration.		
	$= 20t - \dfrac{kt^2}{2} + c$	✓				
	$20 \times 0 - \dfrac{k \times 0^2}{2} + c = 2$			Find constant of integration.	Remember to add c, the constant of integration.	
	$\Rightarrow c = 2$	✓				
	$20 \times 1 - \dfrac{k \times 1^2}{2} + 2 = 15$			Find value of k.	Substitute $h = 2$ and $t = 0$ into the result of the integration to find the value of c.	
	$\Rightarrow \dfrac{1}{2}k = 7$					
	$\Rightarrow k = 14$	✓				
	$h = 20t - 7t^2 + 2$	✓	6	Express h in terms of t.		
10 a)	$\cos ABD = \cos(2x + x)$	✓		Use $\cos ABD = \cos(2x + x)$.	The diagram shows that angle $ABD = 2x + x$, so $\cos ABD = \cos(2x + x)$.	Ch 11
	$= \cos 2x \cos x - \sin 2x \sin x$	✓		Use addition formula.	Use the expansions for $\cos(A + B)$ and $\cos 2A$ from the formula list.	
	$= (2\cos^2 x - 1)\cos x - (2\sin x \cos x)\sin x$	✓		Use double angle formulae.		
	$= 2\cos^3 x - \cos x - 2\sin^2 x \cos x$			Expand brackets and use $\sin^2 x = 1 - \cos^2 x$.	Use $\sin^2 x = 1 - \cos^2 x$ from the National 5 course.	
	$= 2\cos^3 x - \cos x - 2(1 - \cos^2 x)\cos x$	✓				
	$= 2\cos^3 x - \cos x - 2\cos x + 2\cos^3 x$			Expand brackets and rearrange into required form.	Since the answer is given, show all the steps leading to it.	
	$= 4\cos^3 x - 3\cos x$	✓	5			
b)	$\dfrac{1}{4}\int(\cos 3x + 3\cos x)\,dx$	✓		Use $\cos^3 x = \dfrac{1}{4}(\cos 3x + 3\cos x)$.	Make $\cos^3 x$ the subject of the answer to part a). Hence rewrite the integral in a form that can be integrated.	Ch 15
	$= \dfrac{1}{4}\left(\dfrac{1}{3}\sin 3x + \ldots\ldots\right)$	✓		Integrate first term.		
	$= \dfrac{1}{4}\left(\dfrac{1}{3}\sin 3x + 3\sin x\right) + c$	✓	3	Complete integration.	Remember to add c, the constant of integration.	

Practice Paper B

Paper 1 (non-calculator)

Q.	Working	Mark		Note	Hint	HTP
1	$\dfrac{dy}{dx} = 3 - 2x$ $3 - 2x = 4$ $x = -\dfrac{1}{2}$ $y = 3 \times \left(-\dfrac{1}{2}\right) - \left(-\dfrac{1}{2}\right)^2 = -\dfrac{7}{4}$ $\left(-\dfrac{1}{2}, -\dfrac{7}{4}\right)$	✓ ✓ ✓ ✓	 4	Differentiate. Set derivative equal to 4. Solve equation. State co-ordinates of point.	The gradient of the tangent is $4 \Rightarrow \dfrac{dy}{dx} = 4$.	Ch 13
2	$y = 2 - 3x$ $3x + y = 2$ $3x = 2 - y$ $x = \dfrac{2 - y}{3}$ $g^{-1}(x) = \dfrac{2 - x}{3}$	 ✓ ✓ ✓	 3	Substitute y for $g(x)$ and start to rearrange. Complete rearrangement. State inverse function.	Start by changing the subject of $y = 2 - 3x$ to x. Remember to express $g^{-1}(x)$ in terms of x.	Ch 3
3	$\overrightarrow{PQ} = \begin{pmatrix} 3 \\ 0 \\ -4 \end{pmatrix}$ $|\overrightarrow{PQ}| = 5$ unit vector $= \dfrac{1}{5}\begin{pmatrix} 3 \\ 0 \\ -4 \end{pmatrix}$ or $-\dfrac{1}{5}\begin{pmatrix} 3 \\ 0 \\ -4 \end{pmatrix}$	✓ ✓ ✓	 3	Find components of $\overrightarrow{PQ}$. Find $|\overrightarrow{PQ}|$. Find components of unit vector parallel to $|\overrightarrow{PQ}|$.	$\overrightarrow{PQ} = \mathbf{q} - \mathbf{p}$ The magnitude of a unit vector is 1. If $\mathbf{a} = k\mathbf{b}$ then vectors $\mathbf{a}$ and $\mathbf{b}$ are parallel.	Ch 9
4	$f'(x) = 12(5 - 2x)^2 \ldots\ldots$ $= -24(5 - 2x)^2$ $f'(3) = -24(5 - 2 \times 3)^2$ $= -24$	✓ ✓ ✓	 3	Start to differentiate. Complete differentiation. Evaluate $f'(3)$.	Use the chain rule.	Ch 15

Q.	Working	Mark		Note	Hint	HTP
5	$\int_1^2 \left(\dfrac{1}{3} - t^{-2}\right) dt$	✓		Prepare to integrate.	Rewrite the integral in the form $a - t^n$ before integrating, i.e.	Ch 14
	$= \left[\dfrac{1}{3}t \ldots \ldots \right]_1^2$	✓		Integrate first term.	$\dfrac{t^2 - 3}{3t^2} = \dfrac{t^2}{3t^2} - \dfrac{3}{3t^2}$	
	$= \left[\dfrac{1}{3}t + \dfrac{1}{t}\right]_1^2$	✓		Integrate second term.	$= \dfrac{1}{3} - \dfrac{1}{t^2}$	
	$= \left(\dfrac{2}{3} + \dfrac{1}{2}\right) - \left(\dfrac{1}{3} + 1\right)$	✓		Substitute limits.	$= \dfrac{1}{3} - t^{-2}$	
	$= -\dfrac{1}{6}$	✓	5	Evaluate integral.		
6	$\log_5(x - 1) - \log_5 2^3 = 3$ $\log_5(x - 1) - \log_5 8 = 3$	✓		Use $n \log_a x = \log_a x^n$. Use	Use the laws of logarithms to express the equation in the form $\log_5 f(x) = 3$ then convert into exponential form and solve the resulting equation.	Ch 6
	$\log_5\left(\dfrac{x-1}{8}\right) = 3$	✓		$\log_a x - \log_a y = \log_a \dfrac{x}{y}$.		
	$\dfrac{x-1}{8} = 5^3$	✓		Convert to exponential form.		
	$\dfrac{x-1}{8} = 125$ $x - 1 = 1000$ $x = 1001$	✓	4	Solve for x.		
7	centre $= (3, 2)$	✓		Find co-ordinates of centre of circle.	The tangent is the line through (5, 1) which is perpendicular to the radius hence $m_{\text{tangent}} \times m_{\text{radius}} = -1$. Simplify the equation. (Any equivalent simplified version is acceptable.)	Ch 8
	$m_{\text{radius}} = \dfrac{1-2}{5-3} = -\dfrac{1}{2}$	✓		Find gradient of radius.		
	$m_{\text{tangent}} = 2$ $y - 1 = 2(x - 5)$	✓		Find gradient of tangent. Find equation of tangent.		
	$\Leftrightarrow y - 1 = 2x - 10$ $\Leftrightarrow y = 2x - 9$	✓	4			

Q.	Working	Mark	Note	Hint	HTP
8	$\cos x \cos 60 - \sin x \sin 60$ $= \cos x \times \dfrac{1}{2} - \sin x \times \dfrac{\sqrt{3}}{2}$ $= \dfrac{1}{7} \times \dfrac{1}{2} - \dfrac{\sqrt{48}}{7} \times \dfrac{\sqrt{3}}{2}$ $= \dfrac{1}{14} - \dfrac{4\sqrt{3}}{7} \times \dfrac{\sqrt{3}}{2}$ $= \dfrac{1}{14} - \dfrac{12}{14}$ $= -\dfrac{11}{14}$	✓ ✓ ✓ ✓ ✓ 5	Use addition formula. Substitute exact values of cos 60 and sin 60 into expansion. Substitute exact value of $\cos x$ and $\sin x$ into expansion. Simplify $\sqrt{48}$. Complete proof.	Use the formula for cos (A + B) from the formula list. Use $\cos x = \dfrac{1}{7}$ $= \dfrac{\text{adjacent}}{\text{hypotenuse}}$ and Pythagoras' theorem to sketch an appropriate right-angled triangle and hence deduce the value of $\sin x$. (triangle with sides 7, $\sqrt{48}$, 1 and angle $x°$) Use the exact values of cos 60 and sin 60.	Ch 11 and Ch 10
9	$\overrightarrow{AB} = \begin{pmatrix} 6 \\ 9 \\ 12 \end{pmatrix}$ $\overrightarrow{BC} = \begin{pmatrix} x-7 \\ 6 \\ 8 \end{pmatrix}$ $\Rightarrow \overrightarrow{BC} \dfrac{2}{3} \overrightarrow{AB}$ $\Rightarrow x - 7 = 4$ $\Rightarrow x = 11$	✓ ✓ 2	Find k such that $\overrightarrow{BC} = k\overrightarrow{BC}$. Find value of x.	If A, B and C are collinear then $\overrightarrow{BC} = k\overrightarrow{AB}$	Ch 9
10 a)	$P: x = 0 \Rightarrow y = 3^0 - 3 = -2$ $\Rightarrow P(0, -2)$ $Q: y = 0 \Rightarrow 3^x - 3 = 0$ $\Rightarrow x = 1$ $\Rightarrow Q(1, 0)$	✓ ✓ 2	Find co-ordinates of P. Find co-ordinates of Q.	P is on y-axis so P(0, y). Q is on x-axis so Q(x, 0).	Ch 3

Q.	Working	Mark		Note	Hint	HTP
b)		✓		Reflect in y-axis.	$f(x) \rightarrow f(-x)$	Ch 3
		✓	2	Then vertically compress by a factor of 2 with all points correctly annotated.	$\rightarrow \dfrac{1}{2}f(-x)$ $\Rightarrow (x, y) \rightarrow (-x, y)$ $\rightarrow \left(-x, \dfrac{1}{2}y\right)$ e.g. $(2, 6) \rightarrow (-2, 6)$ $\rightarrow (-2, 3)$	
c)	$(0, ...)$	✓		Horizontal translation 2 units left.	$f(x) \rightarrow f(x+2)$ $\rightarrow f(x+2)+10$	
	$(0, 16)$	✓	2	Vertical translation 10 units up.	$\Rightarrow (x, y) \rightarrow (x-2, y)$ $\rightarrow (x-2, y+10)$	
11	$\displaystyle\int_{\frac{\pi}{6}}^{\frac{\pi}{2}} 4 \sin 2x\, dx$	✓		Correct integral for area above x-axis.	Calculate the areas above and below the x-axis separately then add them together.	Ch 15
	$= \left[-2 \cos 2x\right]_{\frac{\pi}{6}}^{\frac{\pi}{2}}$	✓		Integrate.		
	$= -2\left(\cos \pi - \cos \dfrac{\pi}{3}\right)$			Evaluate integral.		
	$= -2\left(-1 - \dfrac{1}{2}\right)$					
	$= 3$	✓				
	$\displaystyle\int_{\frac{\pi}{2}}^{\frac{3\pi}{4}} 4 \sin 2x\, dx$	✓		Correct integral for area below x-axis.		
	$= \left[-2 \cos 2x\right]_{\frac{\pi}{2}}^{\frac{3\pi}{4}}$			Evaluate integral.		
	$= -2\left(\cos \dfrac{3\pi}{2} - \cos \pi\right)$					
	$= -2(0 + 1)$ $= -2$	✓				
	So area below x-axis $= 2$					
	Total area $= 3 + 2 = 5$ units^2.	✓	6	Evaluate total area.		

Q.	Working	Mark		Note	Hint	HTP
12 a)	$\begin{array}{c c c c c} 1 & 2 & 7 & a & b \\ & & 2 & 9 & a+9 \\ \hline & 2 & 9 & a+9 & a+b+9=0 \end{array}$	✓		Use $x=1$ to obtain equation.	Use synthetic division to obtain a pair of simultaneous equations.	Ch 2
	$\begin{array}{c c c c c} -3 & 2 & 7 & a & b \\ & & -6 & -3 & -3a+9 \\ \hline & 2 & 1 & a-3 & -3a+b+ \\ & & & & 9=20 \end{array}$	✓		Use $x=-3$ to obtain equation.		
	$a+b=-9$ $-3a+b=11$ $4a=-20$	✓		Use simultaneous equations. Find a and b.		
	$a=-5,\, b=-4$	✓	4			
b)	$\begin{array}{c c c c c} 1 & 2 & 7 & -5 & -4 \\ & & 2 & 9 & 4 \\ \hline & 2 & 9 & 4 & 0 \end{array}$	✓		Substitute for a and b then divide by $x-1$.	Start by using synthetic division.	
	$(x-1)(2x^2+9x+4)$	✓		Obtain quadratic factor.		
	$(x-1)(2x+1)(x+4)$	✓	3	Complete factorisation.		
13 a)	$\cos x + \sin x =$ $k(\cos x \cos a + \sin x \sin a)$	✓		Use addition formula.	Use the expansion for $\cos(A-B)$ from the formula list.	Ch 12
	$k\cos a = 1,\ k\sin a = 1$	✓		Equate coefficients.		
	$k = \sqrt{1^2+1^2} = \sqrt{2}$	✓		Find k.		
	$a = \tan^{-1}\left(\dfrac{1}{1}\right) = \dfrac{\pi}{4}$ $\cos x + \sin x$ $= \sqrt{2}\cos\left(x - \dfrac{\pi}{4}\right)$	✓	4	Find a and state expression in required form.		

Q.	Working	Mark		Note	Hint	HTP
b)		✓		Sine curve with maximum value $\sqrt{2}$ and minimum value $-\sqrt{2}$.	Use the answer to part a) to rewrite the equation in terms of $\cos x$ only, then sketch the curve with this equation.	Ch 12
		✓		Maximum t.p. $\left(\dfrac{\pi}{4}, \sqrt{2}\right)$ and minimum t.p. $\left(\dfrac{5\pi}{4}, -\sqrt{2}\right)$.		
		✓		x-intercepts $\left(\dfrac{3\pi}{4}, 0\right)$ and $\left(\dfrac{7\pi}{4}, 0\right)$.		
		✓	4	Endpoints $(0, 1)$ and $(2\pi, 1)$.		

Paper 2

Q.	Working	Mark		Note	Hint	HTP
1	$10 - 3x - x^2 < 0$ $x^2 + 3x - 10 > 0$ $(x+5)(x-2) > 0$ ✓ $x < -5, x > 2$ ✓		2	Factorise. Find correct range of values.	Use a sketch graph of $y = (x+5)(x-2)$ to solve $(x+5)(x-2) > 0$.	Ch 4
2 a)	$f\left(\dfrac{1}{x} - 3\right) = \dfrac{1}{\left(\dfrac{1}{x} - 3\right) + 3}$ ✓ $= \dfrac{1}{\dfrac{1}{x}}$ ✓ $= x$ ✓		3	Start composite process. Find $f(g(x))$. Express in simplest form.	$f(g(x)) = \dfrac{1}{g(x) + 3}$	Ch 3
b)	$g(x) = f^{-1}(x)$ ✓		1	State connection.	$f(f^{-1}(x)) = x$	
3 a)	$A = (2, 0)$ ✓ $B = (10, 15)$ ✓ $AB = \sqrt{(10-2)^2 + (0-15)^2}$ $\quad = 17$ ✓		3	Find co-ordinates of A. Find co-ordinates of B. Find distance between centres.	Find the centres of the circles and then use the distance formula.	Ch 8
b)	$r_A = \sqrt{(-2)^2 + 0^2 - (-60)}$ $\quad = 8$ ✓ $r_B = \sqrt{(-10)^2 + (-15)^2 - 300}$ $\quad = 5$ ✓ gap $= 17 - (8+5) = 4$ ✓		3	Find radius of circle, centre A. Find radius of circle, centre B. Find size of gap.	Subtract the sum of the radii from the distance between the centres.	
4 a)	$\overrightarrow{BE} = \dfrac{1}{4} \overrightarrow{BD}$ ✓ $\Rightarrow \mathbf{e} - \mathbf{b} = \dfrac{1}{4}(\mathbf{d} - \mathbf{b})$ $\Rightarrow \mathbf{e} = \dfrac{1}{4}\mathbf{d} + \dfrac{3}{4}\mathbf{b}$ $\Rightarrow \mathbf{e} = \begin{pmatrix} 3 \\ 2 \\ 5 \end{pmatrix} + \begin{pmatrix} 18 \\ 12 \\ 0 \end{pmatrix}$ $\Rightarrow E(21, 14, 5)$ ✓		2	Interpret ratio. Find co-ordinates of E.	$DE{:}EB = 3{:}1 \Rightarrow \overrightarrow{BE} \dfrac{1}{4}\overrightarrow{BD}$	Ch 9

B

Q.	Working	Mark		Note	Hint	HTP
b)	$\overrightarrow{AD} = \begin{pmatrix} -12 \\ 8 \\ 20 \end{pmatrix}$	✓		Find components of $\overrightarrow{AD}$.	$\overrightarrow{AD} = \mathbf{d} - \mathbf{a}$ and $\overrightarrow{AE} = \mathbf{e} - \mathbf{a}$.	Ch 9
	$\overrightarrow{AE} = \begin{pmatrix} -3 \\ 14 \\ 5 \end{pmatrix}$	✓	2	Find components of $\overrightarrow{AE}$.		
c)	$\cos DAE = \dfrac{\overrightarrow{AD}.\overrightarrow{AE}}{|\overrightarrow{AD}||\overrightarrow{AE}|}$	✓		Use scalar product applied to correct angle.	Use vectors that both point away from the vertex of the angle.	
	$\overrightarrow{AD}.\overrightarrow{AE} = 248$	✓		Find scalar product.		
	$|\overrightarrow{AD}| = \sqrt{608}$	✓		Find $|\overrightarrow{AD}|$.	Don't approximate values of surds, e.g. $\sqrt{608} = 24.7$ as premature rounding may lead to an incorrect final answer.	
	$|\overrightarrow{AE}| = \sqrt{230}$	✓		Find $|\overrightarrow{AE}|$.		
	angle $DAE = 48.5°$	✓	5	Find angle.		
5 a)	$M_{PQ} = \left(\dfrac{1}{2}, \dfrac{5}{2}\right)$	✓		Calculate midpoint of PQ.	The line is perpendicular to PQ so $m_{\text{line}} \times m_{PQ} = -1$ and it passes through the midpoint of PQ.	Ch 7
	$m_{PQ} = 1$	✓		Calculate gradient of PQ.		
	$m_{\text{perp}} = -1$	✓		Calculate gradient of perpendicular.	Since the answer is given, show all the steps from $y - \dfrac{5}{2} = -\left(x - \dfrac{1}{2}\right)$ to the required equation.	
	$y - \dfrac{5}{2} = -\left(x - \dfrac{1}{2}\right)$			Demonstrate result.		
	so $y - \dfrac{5}{2} = -x + \dfrac{1}{2}$					
	so $x + y = 3$	✓	4			
b)	e.g. $x + y = 3$			Start to solve simultaneous equations.	The perpendicular bisector of PQ in part a) and the diameter given in part b) intersect at the centre of the circle. Use simultaneous equations to find the point of intersection.	
	$y = 4x - 7$					
	so $x + 4x - 7 = 3$	✓				
	$x = 2$	✓		Find x.		
	$y = 1$			State co-ordinates of C.		
	so C(2, 1)	✓	3			
c)	$r^2 = (3-2)^2 + (5-1)^2 = 17$	✓		Calculate radius².		Ch 8
	$(x-2)^2 + (y-1)^2 = 17$	✓	2	State equation of circle.		

Q.	Working	Mark		Note	Hint	HTP
6	$y = 2\cos 3x - x^{-3}$	✓		Prepare to differentiate second term.	Express the second term in the form x^n before differentiating.	Ch 15 and Ch 13
	$\dfrac{dy}{dx} = -2\sin 3x\ldots\ldots\ldots$	✓		Start to differentiate first term.	Use the chain rule to differentiate the first term.	
	$\dfrac{dy}{dx} = -6\sin 3x\ldots\ldots\ldots$	✓		Complete differentiation of first term.		
	$\dfrac{dy}{dx} = -6\sin 3x + 3x^{-4}$	✓	4	Differentiate second term.		
7 a)(i)	$A_n = 0.04A_{n-1}\ldots\ldots\ldots$	✓		Start recurrence relation.	Form a recurrence relation wich generates a sequence with a limit.	Ch 5
	$= 0.04A_{n-1} + 2100$	✓	2	Complete recurrence relation.		
(ii)	$L = \dfrac{2100}{1-0.04} = £2187{\cdot}50$	✓	1	Find limit.		
b)	$2400 = \dfrac{2100}{1-a}$	✓		Substitute into limit formula.	Form an equation involving the limit formula.	
	$2400(1-a) = 2100$			Find value of a.		
	$2400 - 2400a = 2100$					
	$2400a = 300$					
	$a = 0125$	✓				
	Rory should spend 87.5% of the money in the account each month.	✓	3	Interpret information and state conclusion.		
8	$f(x) = \displaystyle\int\left(3 - \dfrac{4}{x^2}\right)dx$	✓		Know to integrate.	Integrate $f'(x)$ to obtain $f(x)$, since integration is the inverse of differentiation.	Ch 14
	$= 3x + \dfrac{4}{x} + c$	✓		Integrate.	Remember to add c, the constant of integration.	
	$-1 = 3\times 2 + \dfrac{4}{2} + c$			Substitute for $f(x)$ and x.	Substitute $(2, -1)$ into the result of the integration to find the value of c.	
	$\Leftrightarrow -1 = 6 + 2 + c$					
	$\Rightarrow c = -9$	✓				
	$f(x) = 3x + \dfrac{4}{x} - 9$	✓	4	Express $f(x)$ in terms of x.		
9 a)	$243500 \times e^{0.008\times 10}$	✓		Substitute for t in formula.	In 2015 $t = 10$.	Ch 6
	$= 263780$	✓	2	Evaluate formula.		

Q.	Working	Mark		Note	Hint	HTP
b)	$330000 = 243500e^{0.008t}$	✓		Construct equation.		Ch 6
	$e^{0.008t} = \dfrac{330000}{243500}$	✓		Process equation.	Remember $e^x = y \Leftrightarrow x = \ln y$	
	$0.008t = \ln\left(\dfrac{3300}{2435}\right)$	✓		Write in logarithmic form.		
	$t = \dfrac{\ln\left(\dfrac{3300}{2435}\right)}{0.008}$			Solve to find number of years.	Don't approximate the value of $\ln\left(\dfrac{3300}{2435}\right)$ as premature rounding may lead to an incorrect final answer.	
	$= 38$ years	✓	4			
10	$x^2 - kx + x - k = -1$			Rearrange into standard quadratic form.		Ch 4
	$x^2 + (1-k)x + 1 - k = 0$	✓				
	$b^2 - 4ac = 0$	✓		Use discriminant = 0.	Equal roots so $b^2 - 4ac = 0$.	
	$a = 1, b = 1 - k, c = 1 - k$	✓		Identify a, b and c.		
	$(1-k)^2 - 4(1-k) = 0$			Arrange into standard quadratic form.		
	$k^2 + 2k - 3 = 0$	✓				
	$(k-1)(k+3) = 0$			Find values of k.		
	$k = 1, -3$	✓	5			
11	Method 1			Method 1	Use laws of logarithms to rearrange $y = be^{ax}$ into the form $\log_e y = ax + \log_e b$.	Ch 6
	$\log_e y = \log_e be^{ax}$	✓		Take logs of both sides of equation.		
	$\log_e y = \log_e b + \log_e e^{ax}$			Use	This is the equation of the straight line with gradient a and y-intercept $(0, \log_e b)$.	
	$\log_e y = ax + \log_e b$	✓		$\log_e xy = \log_e x + \log_e y$ and $\log_e e^{ax} = ax\log_e e = ax.$		
	$a = \dfrac{4.5}{3} = 1.5$	✓		Find a.	Remember $\log_e b = y \Leftrightarrow b = e^y$.	
	$\log_e b = 4.5$			Find b.		
	$\Rightarrow b = e^{4.5} = 90$	✓				
	Method 2			Method 2	The straight line has equation $\log_e y = mx + c$. Use laws of logarithms to rearrange this equation into the form $y = be^{ax}$.	
	$\log_e y = 1.5x + 4.5$	✓		State linear equation.		
	$y = e^{1.5x + 4.5}$	✓		Convert to exponential form.		
	$y = e^{1.5x} \times e^{4.5}$	✓		Use law of indices.	Remember $\log_e y = x \Leftrightarrow y = e^x$.	
	$y = 90e^{1.5x}$	✓	4	Obtain result.		

Answers B

51

Q.	Working	Mark		Note	Hint	HTP
12 a)	$a = v'(t)$ $= 5 - 2t$	✓ ✓	2	Know to differentiate. Differentiate.	Acceleration is the rate of change of velocity with respect to time i.e. $a = v'(t)$.	Ch 13
b)	$5 - 2t < 0$ $t > 2.5$ After 2.5 seconds	✓ ✓	2	Set up inequality. Solve inequality and interpret result.		
c)	$s(t) = \int v(t)\, dt$ $= t + \dfrac{5}{2}t^2 - \dfrac{1}{3}t^3 + c$ $s(0) = 2 \Rightarrow c = 2$ $\Rightarrow s(t) = t + \dfrac{5}{2}t^2 - \dfrac{1}{3}t^3 + 2$	✓ ✓ ✓	3	Know to integrate. Integrate. Determine constant and state $s(t)$.	Velocity is the rate of change of displacement with respect to time i.e. $v = s'(t)$ so $s = \int v(t)\, dt$. Remember to add c, the constant of integration. Substitute $s = 2$ and $t = 0$ into the result of the integration to find the value of c.	Ch 14
13	$2\cos^2\theta - 1 + \cos\theta = 0$ $2\cos^2\theta + \cos\theta - 1 = 0$ $(2\cos\theta - 1)(\cos\theta + 1) = 0$ $\cos\theta = \dfrac{1}{2}, \cos\theta = -1$ $\theta = \dfrac{\pi}{3}, \dfrac{5\pi}{3}, \pi$	✓ ✓ ✓ ✓	4	Use double angle formula. Rearrange and factorise. Solve for $\cos\theta$. Solve for θ.	Use the substitution $\cos 2\theta = 2\cos^2\theta - 1$ to obtain an equation with terms in $\cos\theta$ only. Use exact values to give the answers in terms of π.	Ch 11

Practice Paper C

Paper 1 (non-calculator)

Q.	Working	Mark		Note	Hint	HTP
1	$\dfrac{dy}{dx} = 4x^3 - 6x + 1$	✓		Differentiate.	The gradient of the tangent is the value of $\dfrac{dy}{dx}$ when $x = -1$.	Ch 13
	at $x = -1$,			Evaluate derivative.		
	$\dfrac{dy}{dx} = -4 - (-6) + 1 = 3$	✓				
	$y = 1 - 3 + (-1) + 5 = 2$	✓		Evaluate y-co-ordinate.	Simplify the equation. (Any equivalent simplified version is acceptable.)	
	$y - 2 = 3\big(x - (-1)\big)$			Find equation of tangent.		
	so $y = 3x + 5$	✓	4			
2 a)	$28 = 40a + b$	✓		Form equation connecting u_0 and u_1.	$u_1 = au_0 + b \Rightarrow u_1 = 28, u_0 = 40$	Ch 5
	$19 = 28a + b$	✓		Form equation connecting u_0 and u_1.	$u_2 = au_1 + b \Rightarrow u_2 = 19, u_1 = 28$	
	$12a = 9$			Find value of a.		
	$a = \dfrac{3}{4}$	✓				
	$28 = 40 \times \dfrac{3}{4} + b$			Find value of b.		
	$28 = 30 + b$					
	$b = -2$	✓	4			
b)	$L = \dfrac{-2}{1 - \dfrac{3}{4}}$	✓		Substitute into limit formula.	$-2 \div \dfrac{1}{4} = -2 \times \dfrac{4}{1} = -8$	
	$= \dfrac{-2}{\dfrac{1}{4}} = -8$	✓	2	Find limit.		

C

Q.	Working	Mark	Note	Hint	HTP
3	$\overrightarrow{VT} = \overrightarrow{VP} + \overrightarrow{PQ} + \overrightarrow{QT}$ $= \overrightarrow{VP} + \overrightarrow{PQ} + \frac{3}{4}\overrightarrow{PS}$	✓	Express $\overrightarrow{VT}$ in terms of $\overrightarrow{VP}$, $\overrightarrow{PQ}$ and $\overrightarrow{QT}$.	Vectors which have the same direction and magnitude are equal, e.g. $\overrightarrow{QR} = \overrightarrow{PS}$.	Ch 9
	$= \begin{pmatrix} -6 \\ -11 \\ -9 \end{pmatrix} + \begin{pmatrix} 5 \\ 5 \\ -5 \end{pmatrix} + \frac{3}{4}\begin{pmatrix} 4 \\ 4 \\ 8 \end{pmatrix}$	✓	Find components of $\overrightarrow{VP}$, $\overrightarrow{PQ}$ and $\overrightarrow{QT}$.		
	$= \begin{pmatrix} 2 \\ -3 \\ -8 \end{pmatrix}$	✓ 3	Find components of $\overrightarrow{VT}$.		
4	$m_{PQ} = \frac{10-1}{4-(-2)} = \frac{9}{6} = \frac{3}{2}$	✓	Find gradient of PQ.	Opposite sides of a parallelogram are parallel and therefore have the same gradient.	Ch 7
	$\Rightarrow m_{RS} = \frac{3}{2}$		Start to find equation of RS.	Since the answer is given, show all the steps leading to the required answer.	
	$y - (-5) = \frac{3}{2}(x-6)$ $2y + 10 = 3x - 18$ $3x - 2y = 28$	✓ ✓ 3	Find equation of RS in required form.		
5	$\int (x^3 + x^{\frac{3}{2}})\,dx$	✓	Prepare to integrate.	Rearrange integral into the form $ax^n + bx^m$ before integrating i.e. $x(x^2 + x^{\frac{1}{2}}) = x^3 + x^{\frac{3}{2}}$.	Ch 14
	$= \frac{x^4}{4} + ...$	✓	Integrate first term.		
	$= \frac{x^4}{4} + \frac{x^{\frac{5}{2}}}{\frac{5}{2}} + ...$	✓	Integrate second term.		
	$= \frac{x^4}{4} + \frac{2x^{\frac{5}{2}}}{5} + c$	✓ 4	Complete integration.	Remember to add c, the constant of integration.	
6 a)	$5 - (x^2 - 2x)$ $= 5 - [(x-1)^2 - 1]$ $= 5 - (x-1)^2 + 1$ $= 6 - (x-1)^2$	✓ ✓ 2	Start to complete square. Complete process.	Complete the square for $-(x^2 - 2x)$ first, then add the 5 at the end.	Ch 4
b)	maximum value $= 6$	✓	State maximum value.	The minimum value of $(x-1)^2$ is 0.	
	maximum value occurs when $(x-1)^2 = 0$	✓ 2	Give justification.		

Q.	Working	Mark	Note	Hint	HTP
7 a)	**Method 1** $\log_b x$ cuts x-axis at $(1, 0)$ hence $\log_b x \to \log_b(x+a)$ under horizontal translation of 1 unit right ✓ $a = -1$ ✓ $b = 4$ ✓		**Method 1** Identify relevant facts. State value of a. State value of b.	Use the graph of $f(x) = \log_a x$. 	Ch 3
	Method 2 $y = \log_b(x+a)$ $\log_b(2+a) = 0$ ✓ $2 + a = b^0 = 1$ so $a = -1$ ✓ $1 = \log_b(5-1)$ $= \log_b 4$ $4 = b^1$ so $b = 4$ ✓	3	**Method 2** Substitute $(2, 0)$ into $y = \log_b(x + a)$. Find value of a. Find value of b.	Substitute $(2, 0)$ into $y = \log_b(x + a)$ and solve to obtain a, then substitute value of a and $(5, 1)$ into $y = \log_b(x + a)$ and solve to obtain b.	
b)	$x > 1, \ x \in R$ ✓	1	State suitable domain.	The graph contains no points with x-co-ordinate ≤ 1.	Ch 6 and Ch3
c)	✓ ✓	2	Reflect in the line $y = x$ with one point correctly annotated. Second point correctly annotated and image asymptote shown.	$f(x) \to f^{-1}(x)$ $\Rightarrow (x, y) \to (y, x)$ e.g. $(2, 0) \to (0, 2)$ and $x = 1 \to y = 1$	Ch 3
8	$\dfrac{dV}{dr} = 4\pi r^2$ ✓ $4 \times \pi \times 5^2 = 100\pi$ ✓	2	Differentiate. Evaluate derivative at $r = 5$.	The rate of change is given by $\dfrac{dV}{dr}$.	Ch 13
9 a)	$f(x^2 - k) = 2(x^2 - k) + 3$ ✓ $= 2x^2 - 2k + 3$ ✓ $g(2x+3) = (2x+3)^2 - k$ $= 4x^2 + 12x + 9 - k$ ✓	3	Substitute for $g(x)$ in $f(x)$. Find $f(g(x))$ in simplest form. Find $g(f(x))$ in simplest form.	$f(x) = 2x + 3$ $\Rightarrow f(g(x)) = 2(g(x)) + 3$ $g(x) = x^2 - k$ $\Rightarrow g(f(x)) = (f(x))^2 - k$	Ch 3

Q.	Working	Mark	Note	Hint	HTP
b) (i)	$4x^2+12x+9-k$ $\quad -(2x^2-2k+3)$ $=4x^2+12x+9-k$ $\quad -2x^2+2k-3$ $=2x^2+12x+6+k$	✓ 1	Show steps leading to required form.	Since the answer is given, show all the steps leading to it.	Ch 3
(ii)	$b^2-4ac=0$ $a=2, b=12, c=6+k$ $144-8(6+k)=0$ $96-8k=0$ $8k=96$ $k=12$	✓ ✓ ✓ 3	Use discriminant $=0$. Identify a, b and c. Find k.	Equal roots so $b^2-4ac=0$.	Ch 2
10	**Method 1** $\log_3 y = \log_3 kx^n$ $\log_3 y = n\log_3 x + \log_3 k$ $\log_3 k = 2$ $k=3^2=9$ $n=-\dfrac{1}{4}$ **Method 2** $\log_3 y = -\dfrac{1}{4}\log_3 x + 2$ $\log_3 y = -\dfrac{1}{4}\log_3 x + \log_3 3^2$ $\log_3 y = -\dfrac{1}{4}\log_3 x + \log_3 9$ $\log_3 y = \log_3 x^{-\frac{1}{4}} + \log_3 9$ $\log_3 y = \log_3 9x^{-\frac{1}{4}}$ $y = 9x^{-\frac{1}{4}}$	✓ ✓ ✓ ✓ ✓ ✓ ✓ ✓ ✓ ✓ 5	**Method 1** Take logarithms of both sides of equation. Use $\log_a xy = \log_a x + \log_a y$ and $\log_a x^n = n\log_a x$. Interpret y-intercept. Solve for k. Interpret gradient. **Method 2** State linear equation. Express all terms in terms of $\log_3$. Use $n\log ax = \log_a x^n$. Use $\log_a x + \log_a y = \log_a xy$. Interpret result.	Use the laws of logarithms to rearrange $y=kx^n$ into the form $\log_3 y = n\log_3 x + \log_3 k$. This is the equation of the straight line with gradient n and y-intercept $(0, \log_3 k)$. Remember $\log_3 k = y \Leftrightarrow k = 3^y$. The straight line has equation $\log_3 y = m\log_3 x + c$. Use the laws of logarithms to rearrange this equation into the form $y=kx^n$.	Ch 6
11	$p=3$ $q=40$ $r=-1$	✓ ✓ ✓ 3	State value of p. State value of q. State value of r.	The graph of $y=\cos x$ has been stretched p units vertically, moved q units to the left and r units up.	Ch 10

Q.	Working	Mark		Note	Hint	HTP
12	$\left[....\sin\left(3\theta-\dfrac{\pi}{4}\right)\right]_{\frac{\pi}{6}}^{\frac{5\pi}{12}}$	✓		Start to integrate.	Use $\displaystyle\int\cos(ax+b)\,dx$ $=\dfrac{1}{a}\sin(ax+b)+c$	Ch 15
	$\left[\dfrac{1}{3}\sin\left(3\theta-\dfrac{\pi}{4}\right)\right]_{\frac{\pi}{6}}^{\frac{5\pi}{12}}$	✓		Complete integration.		
	$\dfrac{1}{3}\sin\left(\dfrac{15\pi}{12}-\dfrac{\pi}{4}\right)-$ $\dfrac{1}{3}\sin\left(\dfrac{3\pi}{6}-\dfrac{\pi}{4}\right)$	✓		Substitute limits.	Use exact values of $\sin\pi$ and $\sin\dfrac{\pi}{4}$ and, since the answer is given, show all the steps leading to the required answer.	
	$=\dfrac{1}{3}\sin\pi-\dfrac{1}{3}\sin\dfrac{\pi}{4}$ $=\dfrac{1}{3}\times0-\dfrac{1}{3}\times\dfrac{1}{\sqrt{2}}$			Evaluate.		
	$=-\dfrac{1}{3\sqrt{2}}$	✓				
	$=-\dfrac{1}{3\sqrt{2}}\times\dfrac{\sqrt{2}}{\sqrt{2}}$			Express in required form.		
	$=-\dfrac{\sqrt{2}}{6}$	✓	5			
13	$e^{x+1}-e^x=1$ $e^x(e-1)=1$	✓		Gather like terms and factorise.	Make e^x the subject and then take natural logarithms of both sides of the equation.	Ch 6
	$e^x=\dfrac{1}{e-1}$	✓		Solve for e^x.	Since the answer is given, show all the steps leading to the required answer.	
	$x=\log_e\left(\dfrac{1}{e-1}\right)$	✓	3	Take natural logarithms of both sides of equation.		

Q.	Working	Mark		Note	Hint	HTP
14 a)	$x^2 + (y-t)^2 = 9$	✓	1	State equation of circle.		Ch 8
b)	$x^2 + (x-t)^2 = 9$	✓		Substitute $y = x$ into the equation of the circle.	Use simultaneous equations (substitution method) to find the point of contact of the line and the circle.	Ch 8 and Ch 4
	$2x^2 - 2xt + t^2 - 9 = 0$			Rearrange into standard form and use discriminant = 0.		
	$b^2 - 4ac = 0$	✓			There is only one point of contact so $b^2 - 4ac = 0$.	
	$a = 2, b = -2t, c = t^2 - 9$	✓		Identify a, b and c.		
	$4t^2 - 8(t^2 - 9) = 0$			Find t in simplest form.		
	$-4t^2 + 72 = 0$					
	$t^2 = 18$					
	$t = 3\sqrt{2}$	✓	4			

Paper 2

Q.	Working	Mark	Note	Hint	HTP
1 a)	$7 - 4x < 0$ $4x > 7$ $x > \dfrac{7}{4}$	✓ 1	State range of values.	$f(x)$ is undefined when $7 - 4x < 0$.	Ch 3
b)	$y = \dfrac{x^3 + 1}{2}$ $2y = x^3 + 1$ $x^3 = 2y - 1$ $x = \sqrt[3]{2y - 1}$ $g^{-1}(x) = \sqrt[3]{2x - 1}$	✓ ✓ ✓ 3	Substitute y for $f(x)$ and start to rearrange. Complete rearrangement. State inverse function.	Start by changing the subject of $y = \dfrac{x^3 + 1}{2}$ to x. Remember to express $g^{-1}(x)$ in terms of x.	Ch 3
2 a)	$M_{BD} = (8, 2)$ $M_{BD} = -\dfrac{3}{2}$ $m_{perp} = \dfrac{2}{3}$ $y - 2 = \dfrac{2}{3}(x - 8)$ $3y - 6 = 2x - 16$ $2x - 3y = 10$	✓ ✓ ✓ ✓ 4	Calculate midpoint of BD. Calculate gradient of BD. Calculate gradient of perpendicular. Find equation of AC.	AC is the perpendicular bisector of BD. Simplify the equation. (Any equivalent simplified version is acceptable.)	Ch 7
b) (i)	e.g. $5x - y = 64$ $2x - 3y = 10$ so $15x - 3y = 192$ $2x - 3y = 10$ (14, 6)	✓ ✓ 2	Start to solve simultaneous equations. Find co-ordinates of point of intersection.	Use simultaneous equations to find the point of intersection of AC and DC.	
(ii)	$\tan \theta = 5$ $\theta = 78.7°$	✓ ✓ 2	Use $m = \tan \theta$. Calculate angle.	$\tan \theta = m_{DC}$	

Q.	Working	Mark		Note	Hint	HTP
3	$C_1(-3, 5)$	✓		Find centre of given circle.	Find the centre and radius of the circle whose equation is given, then use these to find the centre and radius of the other circle.	Ch 8
	$r_1 = \sqrt{(3^2 + (-5)^2 - 14)} = \sqrt{20}$	✓		Find radius of given circle.		
	$\overrightarrow{C_1P} = \begin{pmatrix} 4 \\ -2 \end{pmatrix} \Rightarrow \overrightarrow{PC_2} = \begin{pmatrix} 2 \\ -1 \end{pmatrix}$			Find centre of other circle.		
	$\Rightarrow C_2(3, 2)$	✓				
	$r_2 = \frac{1}{2}\sqrt{20} = \frac{1}{2} \times 2\sqrt{5} = \sqrt{5}$	✓		Find radius of other circle.		
	$(x-3)^2 + (y-2)^2 = 5$	✓	5	State equation of other circle.	The brackets need not be expanded.	
4	$y = (1+x^2)^{\frac{1}{2}} + \sin^2 x$	✓		Prepare to differentiate first term.	Express the first term in the form $(1+x^2)^n$ and then use the chain rule to differentiate both terms.	Ch 15
	$\frac{dy}{dx} = \frac{1}{2}(1+x^2)^{-\frac{1}{2}} \dotsc\dotsc\dotsc$	✓		Start to differentiate first term.		
	$= x(1+x^2)^{-\frac{1}{2}} \dotsc\dotsc\dotsc$	✓		Complete differentiation of first term.		
	$= x(1+x^2)^{-\frac{1}{2}} + 2\sin x \dotsc\dotsc$	✓		Start to differentiate second term.		
	$= x(1+x^2)^{-\frac{1}{2}} + 2\sin x \cos x$	✓	5	Complete differentiation of second term.		
5		✓		Roots at -2 and 2.	Stationary points of $f(x)$ are roots of $f'(x)$. The graph of $f'(x)$ is above the x-axis where the gradient of $f(x)$ is positive and below the x-axis where the gradient of $f(x)$ is negative.	Ch 13
		✓		Turning point at $(-2, 0)$.		
		✓	3	Correct shape.		

Q.	Working	Mark	Note	Hint	HTP
6	$2 + x - x^2 = 2 + 9x - 3x^2$	✓	Form equation to find limits.	Use $\int_a^b$ upper - lower.	Ch 14
	$2x^2 - 8x = 0$		Find limits.	The limits are the x-co-ordinates of the points of intersection of the two curves.	
	$2x(x-4) = 0$				
	$x = 0, x = 4$	✓			
	$\int_0^4 (2 + 9x - 3x^2 - (2 + x - x^2))\, dx$		Correct integral for area.		
	$= \int_0^4 (8x - 2x^2)\, dx$	✓			
	$= \left[4x^2 - \dfrac{2x^3}{3} \right]_0^4$	✓	Integrate.		
	$= \left(4 \times 4^2 - \dfrac{2 \times 4^3}{3} \right) - 0$	✓	Substitute limits.		
	$= 21\dfrac{1}{3}\ \text{units}^2$	✓ 6	Find area.		
7	$6 \sin x \cos x = 2 \cos x$	✓	Use double angle formula.	Use the substitution $\sin 2x = 2 \sin x \cos x$.	Ch 11
	$6 \sin x \cos x - 2 \cos x = 0$		Rearrange and factorise.		
	$2 \cos x (3 \sin x - 1) = 0$	✓			
	$\cos x = 0,\ \sin x = \dfrac{1}{3}$	✓	Solve for $\cos x$ and $\sin x$.		
	$19.5 \qquad 160.5$				
	$x = 90, 270, 195$ and 1605	✓ 4	Solve for x.		
8	$a = 2$	✓	Find a.	Since $x = -2$ and $x = 1$ are roots, then $x + 2$ and $x - 1$ are factors.	Ch 2
	$b = -1$	✓	Find b.		
	$(-1, 12) \Rightarrow 12 = k(-1 + 2)(-1 - 1)^2$		Calculate k.	Since $(-1, 12)$ is on the graph, substitute $x = -1$ and $y = 12$ into the resulting equation to calculate k.	
	$12 = 4k$				
	$k = 3$	✓ 3			

Q.	Working	Mark		Note	Hint	HTP
9 a)	$2 \mid$ 1 −9 24 −20	✓		Set up top row of synthetic division table.	Use synthetic division to show that $f(2) = 0$.	Ch 2

	$2 \mid$ 1 −9 24 −20
	          2 −14 20
	      1 −7 10 $\mid$ 0
				Complete table and state conclusion.	Remember to state the conclusion with justification.	

	$f(2) = 0$ so $(x − 2)$ is a factor	✓	2			
b)	$(x − 2)(x^2 − 7x + 10) = 0$	✓		Find quadratic factor.		
	$(x − 2)(x − 2)(x − 5) = 0$	✓		Factorise completely.		
	$x = 2, 5$	✓	3	Find roots.		
10	$f'(x) = 3x^2 + 2x − 5$	✓		Differentiate.	The maximum and minimum values occur either at the maximum or minimum turning point in the interval or at the endpoints of the interval.	Ch 13
	$3x^2 + 2x − 5 = 0$	✓		Set derivative equal to zero.		
	$(3x + 5)(x − 1) = 0$	✓		Factorise derivative.		
	$x = -\dfrac{5}{3},\ x = 1$	✓		Solve equation.		
	$f(1) = 1 + 1 − 5 − 2 = −5$	✓		Evaluate f at relevant stationary point.		
	$f(0) = −2$			Evaluate f at endpoints of interval.		
	$f(4) = 64 + 16 − 20 − 2 = 58$	✓				
	maximum = 58, minimum = −5	✓	7	State maximum and minimum values.		

Q.	Working	Mark	Note	Hint	HTP
11 a)	$\sqrt{3}\cos x + \sin x =$	✓	Use addition formula.	Use the expansion for $\cos(A-B)$ from the formula list.	Ch 12
	$k(\cos x\cos a + \sin x\sin a)$				
	$k\cos a = \sqrt{3},\ k\sin a = 1$	✓	Equate coefficients.		
	$k = \sqrt{\sqrt{3}^2 + 1^2} = 2$	✓	Find k.		
	$a = \tan^{-1}\left(\dfrac{1}{\sqrt{3}}\right) = 30$		Find a and state expression in required form.		
	$\sqrt{3}\cos x - \sin x =$				
	$2\cos(x-30)$	✓ 4			
b)	$220 + 140\cos(30t-30)°$	✓ 1	State equation.	Use the answer to part a) to express d in terms of $\cos 30t°$ only.	
c)	$d = 220 + 140 \times(-1) = 80$ cm	✓	Find depth at 'low-water'.	Use the answer to part b) and your knowledge of the cosine graph to find the minimum value of d.	
	$30t - 30 = 180$		Find time of 'low-water'.		
	so $t = 7$				
	i.e. time = 0700	✓ 2			
12 a)	$\overrightarrow{AE} = \dfrac{5}{9}\overrightarrow{AC}$	✓	Interpret ratio.		Ch 9
	$\Rightarrow \mathbf{e} - \mathbf{a} = \dfrac{5}{9}(\mathbf{c}-\mathbf{a})$		Find co-ordinates of E.		
	$\mathbf{e} = \dfrac{5}{9}\left(\begin{pmatrix} 8 \\ 9 \\ 6 \end{pmatrix} - \begin{pmatrix} -1 \\ 0 \\ -3 \end{pmatrix}\right) + \begin{pmatrix} -1 \\ 0 \\ -3 \end{pmatrix}$			Remember to give the final answer as co-ordinates not components.	
	$\Rightarrow E(4,5,2)$	✓ 2			

Q.	Working	Mark	Note	Hint	HTP
b)	$\overrightarrow{BE} = \begin{pmatrix} 2 \\ -1 \\ 8 \end{pmatrix}$	✓	Find the components of $\overrightarrow{BE}$.		Ch 9
	$\overrightarrow{ED} = \begin{pmatrix} 4 \\ -2 \\ 16 \end{pmatrix}$		Find components of $\overrightarrow{ED}$ and express as a multiple of $\overrightarrow{BE}$.	Conclusion must use the words 'parallel', 'common point' and 'collinear' appropriately.	
	$\Rightarrow \overrightarrow{ED} = 2\overrightarrow{BE}$	✓			
	so BE and ED are parallel, and since E is a common point, then B, E and D are collinear	✓ 3	Correct conclusion.		
c)	$\cos A\widehat{E}B = \dfrac{\overrightarrow{EA}.\overrightarrow{EB}}{|\overrightarrow{EA}||\overrightarrow{EB}|}$	✓	Use scalar product applied to correct angle.	Use vectors that both point away from the vertex of the angle.	
	$\overrightarrow{EA}.\overrightarrow{EB} = 45$	✓	Find scalar product.		
	$\left|\overrightarrow{EA}\right| = \sqrt{75}$	✓	Find $\left|\overrightarrow{EA}\right|$.	Don't approximate values of surds, e.g. $\sqrt{75} = 8.7$ as premature rounding may lead to an incorrect final answer.	
	$\left|\overrightarrow{EB}\right| = \sqrt{69}$	✓	Find $\left|\overrightarrow{EB}\right|$.		
	angle AEB = 51.3°	✓ 5	Find angle AEB.		
13	$\dfrac{2\sin x \cos x}{1 + \cos 2x}$	✓	Use $\sin 2x = 2\sin x \cos x$.	Use formulae for $\sin 2x$ and $\cos 2x$.	Ch 11
	$= \dfrac{2\sin x \cos x}{1 + 2\cos^2 x - 1}$	✓	Use $\cos 2x = 2\cos^2 x - 1$.		
	$= \dfrac{2\sin x \cos x}{2\cos^2 x}$		Show all remaining steps to complete proof.	Since the answer is given, show all the steps leading to the required answer.	
	$= \dfrac{\sin x}{\cos x}$				
	$= \tan x$	✓ 3			